C000173619

To Kathleen Sl

with Best Wishes

Kenneth M'Keown

COM 1994

A Tale of Two Citadels

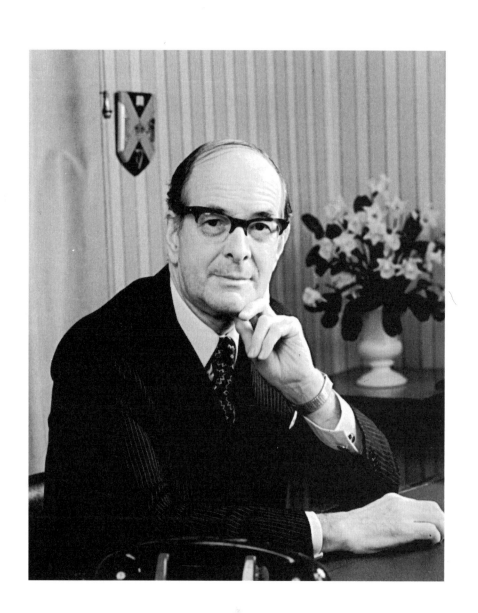

A Tale of Two Citadels

Memoirs of a Surgeon and His Times

by Kenneth C. McKeown

with appreciations of the author by
Professor R. A. Macbeth
Professor Sir Christopher Booth, MD, FRCP
Professor Reg Hall, CBE, MD, FRCP

The Pentland Press
Edinburgh–Cambridge–Durham

I am indebted to my secretary, Lyn Proud, for her tireless work

© Kenneth C. McKeown, 1994

First published in 1994
by The Pentland Press Ltd
1 Hutton Close
South Church .
Bishop Auckland
Durham

ISBN 1–85821–208–1

Typeset by Carnegie Publishing Ltd, 18 Maynard St, Preston
Printed and bound in Great Britain by Bookcraft (Bath) Ltd

Contents

Illustrations

The Author – Three
Appreciations

IT WAS WITH much pleasure and anticipation that I learned that Kenneth McKeown was preparing his autobiography; pleasure because of my admiration for the individual, and anticipation since I have long sought an answer as to how one man converted the hospital in a relatively small industrial town in north-east England into an internationally recognised centre of surgical excellence. In the introduction to his autobiography, the only part of the manuscript that I have thus far had the opportunity to read, he credits the initiation of the National Health Service with the creation of District General Hospitals in which patients: wherever they live (may) obtain as high a standard of treatment . . . as that which could be obtained in any of the Teaching Hospitals. While this, in theory, is doubtless accurate it is a self-evident truth that enabling legislation can not, of itself, produce excellence in medical care. Excellence depends on the presence of an individual or a group of individuals dedicated to the provision of exemplary medical care, a situation created at the Darlington Memorial Hospital with the appointment of Kenneth McKeown in 1950.

While I feel both honoured and, at the same time, inadequate in responding to the request to provide an international perspective in regard to this portrait of the author, I have perhaps one qualification that sets me apart from most, and perhaps all, other friends and admirers of Kenneth McKeown from beyond the borders of the United Kingdom who might represent the international surgical community. In 1973 I had the privilege of being a part of the McKeown surgical team. I was, at the time, a mature academic surgeon in search of a period of restoration as a clinical surgeon following nine months of a sabbatical year spent in a very non-clinical and non-English-speaking environment. The choice of Darlington resulted from my enquiries directed to academic surgical colleagues as to where in Britain I should go to observe, and participate in the activities of, a master surgeon. Their answer was unanimous and unequivocal: Mr. Kenneth McKeown in Darlington. Others outside of Britain have, I know, followed his impressive surgical career through his publications, his presentations at scientific meetings and as a consequence of his extensive travels and visits to fellow surgeons in their own centres. However few, I suspect, have had the intimate and stimulating personal experience that I have enjoyed and which may qualify me as a participant in presenting one part of his portrait.

While surgery is much more than a technical craft, the performance of the procedure itself is the central and critical component of surgical management and in this regard Kenneth McKeown is indeed a master and a perfectionist. In the operating theatre one soon comes to appreciate, as I have previously recorded, that he has been born with or has somehow acquired: "a gentleness and a feeling for human tissue that permits invariable and easy access to the natural, relatively bloodless, tissue planes which the master instinctively enters but which the average surgeon never seems to find, or finds fortuitously only on rare occasions." An operation performed by a master surgeon is beautiful to observe and, what is even more important, the patients fare far better. In Darlington in the 1970s, although major intra-thoracic and intra-abdominal extirpative surgery for cancer constituted a large part of the surgery performed, there was not even an intensive care unit nor was there any indication of a need for one. When an operation is done "right" by a master surgeon the patient is virtually assured of an uncomplicated convalescence and there is little need for such a unit.

In his summary of his book Kenneth McKeown expresses the hope that it may appeal to the younger physician or surgeon by providing a window on the personalities "of some of the great masters of surgery . . . whose names are now legend". While this will, without doubt, add interest and colour to the narrative one hopes that the major message that younger members of the profession will acquire from this very personal story is the satisfaction that the practice of medicine can provide to one individual dedicated to the achievement of excellence, and equally through the unparalleled opportunity given to truly become involved with a supportive of one's fellow man. At first sight a consultant surgical practice may not appear to be the ideal milieu in which empathy and sincere concern for the welfare of one's patients can flourish. Perhaps too this may be easier to achieve in a provincial setting than in a teaching hospital in a large urban centre. In any event, Kenneth McKeown's knowledge of, interest in and concern for those persons entrusted to his care is an example of the doctor-patient relationship as it should be. One can only hope that this becomes apparent to those who read the book and that the career depicted will come to serve as a stimulus and role model, particularly for those starting out in the profession. Technical excellence, on the one hand, and empathy and compassion, on the other, are not two mutually exclusive "Citadels" nor are they "Two Solitudes" as seems so often to be true today. Rather the practice of the two in harmony and unison is the mark of true surgical perfection.

However, no individual can achieve excellence alone, at least in relation to surgical care. Its achievement must be a team effort and in creating a completely new surgical unit in a provincial town where none previously existed the ability to choose highly competent colleagues and to earn their loyalty and support in developing such a smooth functioning unit is essential. Seldom does one see a group of anaesthetists, surgeons-in-training and nurses, both ward and operating room, so admiring of and so united behind their chief as was true of the surgical group I observed in Darlington. I soon came to appreciate that the team was an essential component in the unit's success in a subtle way which I had been unaware of when observing other surgical units. One got the impression that Kenneth McKeown was so intensely and single-mindedly focused on the operative and overall care of his patients that he had little time for, and little apparent interest in, those peripheral activities, whether medically related or personal, which could be left to trusted associates.

The list of those whose support was essential to what he was able to achieve begins first and foremost with his wife, Joan, who relieved him of so many personal concerns; his secretary, Eileen, who relieved him of much of the essential but clinically dispensable administrative tasks; as well as the surgical team members previously mentioned.

Finally it remains to be recorded that Joan and Kenneth McKeown are charming and gracious hosts and guests. Next to being in an operating theatre one suspects that another of Kenneth's great joys is driving with

Joan in a new smooth-running Jaguar while showing off his beloved Yorkshire Dales to an appreciative surgical guest. His surgical colleagues around the world know Kenneth McKeown, master surgeon, well. We look forward to learning more of the man hidden within the surgeon in *A Tale of Two Citadels.*

Robert A. Macbeth B.A., M.D., M.Sc., D.Sc. (Hon.), F.A.C.S., F.R.C.S.
Formerly   : Professor and Chairman, Department of Surgery, University of Alberta
            : Chief Executive Officer, Canadian Cancer Society and the National Cancer Institute of Canada
            : Chief Executive Officer, Hannah Institute for the History of Medicine

THE ESTABLISHMENT of the National Health Service in 1948 led to major developments in the practice of medicine. During the early years of the service, it was undeniably the introduction of specialist services, based on district general hospitals throughout the country, that was its most immediate and significant achievement. The reform of general practice was to come later.

In the pre-war years and until the foundation of the NHS much surgery in country districts and provincial towns was often undertaken by part-time general practitioners with little or no training. Operations were not infrequently carried out in parlours or on kitchen tables. For an individual such as myself, working for much of my professional career in the elitist medical environment of a London postgraduate hospital where specialists congregate, it has been both fascinating and encouraging to observe how gifted individuals, trained in the traditions of those institutions, have built up specialist units, often in surgery, which have come to rival if not excel the reputations of many so-called "centres of excellence", as the major teaching hospitals like to style themselves.

When Kenneth McKeown left the cloistered world of London medicine in 1950 to establish a surgical service in Darlington, Northallerton and the Northeast, the people of that region had to travel to Leeds, Newcastle and farther afield to obtain surgical treatment. Furthermore, there was widespread concern about hospital treatment, reference to hospital in my native Wensleydale being regarded in those days as almost a death sentence. In the more than four decades that have passed since McKeown began to practice his surgical skills in the Northeast, he has achieved so much. Not only has a highly effective and efficient surgical service been set up, for the great benefit of those who have the good fortune to live in his area, but he himself and his unit have become internationally recognised. He has created a "centre of excellence" in its own right, not only for surgical practice but also for outstanding research. As one who has been both a professor in a well-known medical department in London and director of a Medical Research Council Centre for Clinical Research, I can testify that any London teaching hospital, or indeed any other teaching institution anywhere in the world, would have been proud to tempt Kenneth McKeown away from the Northeast that he has come to love so much. It is to his great credit and to the benefit of those whom he has served, that he has always stuck to his last. His national stature is recognised by the many honours he has received. More significantly, surgeons have come from far and wide to learn his skills in the district general hospitals where he has worked with such devotion through the years. The Northeast, and that includes my own family, has been well served by this remarkably talented surgeon. Not only that, he can tell us all about it. He is an extraordinarily able writer who exuberantly brings to life the joy of using surgical skill for the benefit of mankind.

Sir Christopher Booth M.D. L.L.D. F.R.C.P. (Ed.)
President, British Medical Association 1986–87,
Royal Society of Medicine 1988–90,
and of British Society of Gastroenterology 1978–79

IT GIVES ME great pleasure to pen a few words about my old friend and colleague Kenneth McKeown. We worked together on a number of problem patients in the Newcastle region and I was always enlightened by the combination of his clinical and humane approaches to any problem. His surgical units at the Friarage Hospital Northallerton and at the Memorial Hospital in Darlington were Meccas for oesophageal surgery where patients came from all over the world, often with advanced disease to benefit from his masterly techniques. I find close parallels between his unit and that of Sir Magdi Yacoub at Harefield of which I have personal experience. Both, surgeons of immense technical skill and great personal charisma, created centres of excellence for pioneering surgical advances in small district general hospitals where patients could benefit from their innovative and creative management.

The high regard in which he is held by his colleagues is highlighted by the list of the guest speakers at his Valedictory Seminar – past presidents of The Royal College of Surgeons of England and of Edinburgh, the local Professor of Medicine, and a senior surgeon from Scotland.

Our country is fortunate indeed to have such giants of surgery who are prepared to serve their fellow men. This personal account of his surgical lifetime embodies the excitement and adventures of a long and remarkable career.

Professor Reg Hall, C.B.E., M.D., F.R.C.P. Professor of Medicine Emeritus, University of Wales College of Medicine, Cardiff. Formerly Professor of Medicine, Newcastle-upon-Tyne.

Introduction

THE medical profession has its roots deep in the learning and philosophy of centuries past. Though some of its origins are from the ancient civilisations of China and of Egypt, Hippocrates (460 BC) the Greek physician is regarded as the father of modern medicine. He himself was from a long line of physicians being seventeenth descendent of Aesculapius, the physician whose sign of the staff intertwined with the serpent is the heraldic symbol and logo of medical societies throughout the world today.

Trained in Athens, Hippocrates left this centre of learning to establish his practice in the Greek Island of Cos. Like a Grecian arch he founded medicine on the pillars of clinical observation and a code of behaviour. Over subsequent centuries clinical observation has been the basis of medical teaching, while his code of ethics has been incorporated in the Hippocratic Oath which until recently had to be sworn by all graduates in medicine.

From these roots in antiquity the profession has grown into a self regulating institution of high integrity. Its academic standards have been guaranteed by the Universities and by the Royal Colleges, while the responsibilities and discipline of its members have been controlled by the General Medical Council.

The profession has gained and retained the confidence of the public, and it is to the doctor that people turn in times of illness or distress. This doctor–patient relationship has been of the greatest importance. It enables the patient to have confidence and trust in his doctor and to know that he will obtain the best available treatment and will be sustained and supported throughout his illness.

I

It is the clinical need of the patient that is paramount and not the cost of treatment. This doctor–patient relationship is unique amongst all the professions and is a much closer bond than that which exists between a lawyer and his client, or a teacher and his pupil.

A self-critical image of the medical profession between the two world wars has been portrayed by Dr A. J. Cronin who, while failing to attain his highest aspirations in medicine, reached his zenith of achievement as the author of *The Citadel*. Implicit in this title is the criticism that the profession is a stronghold designed to protect its self-interest and to dominate the conduct of its members. This book has greatly influenced political thinking and has sown the seed from which the present medical predicament has grown. It has been a major factor in the introduction of a political dimension into medical care.

The horror and destruction in cities and on the battlefields during the Second World War disrupted society and its institutions. Medicine itself felt the repercussions of this holocaust and it is not surprising therefore that a vision of a new medical service should arise like Phoenix from the ashes of destruction.

In Britain this vision materialized and was embodied in the formation of The National Health Service (1948). The expectations of patient care in the National Health Service appeared to be without limits and promised a medical Utopia. However, with the passage of time the new service encountered difficulties which, though foreseen by many members of the profession, had not been fully realized by its political masters.

By a strange paradox these difficulties have arisen, not because of the failure of medicine but because of its remarkable successes. Quite dramatic advances in the treatment of disease have thrown financial strains on the resources of a service which is "free at the point of delivery". Advances in medicine have been rapid and have been spread over a very wide field enabling the doctor to attain objectives far beyond the wildest expectations of fifty years ago.

The major clinical problems facing medical science have been those of disease due to infection, cancer in its various forms and degenerative diseases, especially those affecting joints and the heart and the blood vessels. Infective diseases (except AIDS) have been controlled by antibiotics, immunization and by hygiene and public health measures. Medieval disasters such as the plague, appropriately called the Black Death due to Bubonic plague, are now unknown due to better public health. Small pox has been eradicated throughout the world by vaccination, and poliomyelitis (infantile paralysis), that great maimer of children, has almost disappeared in western countries as the result of immunization.

The treatment of cancer has made some headway due to better surgery, radiotherapy, and the newer treatments with chemotherapy. A major breakthrough, in the treatment of malignant disease comparable with the use of antibiotics in infective conditions, has not yet been achieved.

It is encouraging, however, to enumerate the recent advances in medicine. After centuries of unsuccessful attempts at the management of bacterial infections, other than by the use of the lancet or scalpel, the discovery of sulphonamides (the M&B group of drugs) in 1936, followed by the advent of penicillin in 1942 have transformed the scene. Not only can infective conditions be successfully treated medically but the scope of surgery, too, has been enormously increased by their use.

In the treatment of degenerative disease by transplant surgery progress has been equally dramatic. In the absence of a fuller knowledge of the cause of degenerative disease the problem has been approached by the principle of replacement of the affected joint or transplant of the appropriate organ. Hip replacement, first attempted before the Second World War with little success, has now evolved to become one of the most valuable means of restoration of the health of elderly patients and the successful techniques employed in the hip have been extended to other joints. Kidney transplants, initially regarded as a laboratory procedure, are now fully established on a clinical basis and have become a normal routine.

In an even more dramatic advance the invention of the artificial heart has enabled complex cardiac repair operations to be carried out. Narrowed or blocked coronary arteries, the cause of much pain and premature death, can now be dealt with. Diseased arteries can be by-passed and damaged heart valves can be replaced.

Professor Chris Barnard of the Groote Schurr Hospital in Capetown was the first surgeon to show that the entire heart could be replaced. With refinements of technique and the advancements of knowledge, cardiac replacement is becoming more and more common. Even combined lung and heart transplants are being successfully undertaken in ever greater numbers. In the abdomen, liver and pancreatic transplants have been pioneered by Professor Roy Calne at Cambridge* with ever increasing success. All these advances have opened up new frontiers of attainment in the expectation of health and longevity.

It is strange to relate that these great successes have produced the very problems that now face the National Health Service. The techniques involved are extremely expensive in time, skilled manpower, and materials. These successes result in survival of patients who formerly would have died, and this survival has resulted in an ever ageing population with all the social and economic consequences of this change.

Most of the medical advances have been in the hospital aspects of treatment and in an attempt to cope with these problems successive governments have introduced a series of reorganizations of the hospital service. None of these reorganizations have solved the problems associated with the great advances in medical science associated with limited financial resources. The methods used in these reorganizations have been based on reports of various working groups which have been set up to attempt to deal with the problem.

In the first instance a complicated series of co-ordinated and inter-digitating committees was recommended and became know as the "Cog-Wheel" report because of the interdependence of each committee. [1] This system failed because of the slowness of the mechanisms and the failure of committees to take and to implement decisions.

The failure of the committee structure led to a new approach which resulted in a vast expansion of administration both vertical and lateral. Administrators have concentrated on the actual structure of the service which has had the effect of diverting resources and finances away from the actual care of the patient. [2]

Contemporaneously, a new approach, largely based on market and commercial considerations has resulted in administrators being replaced by managers whose major concern is with personnel and with budgets and this has caused a medical and political furore.

Trying to solve problems by reorganization is a process as old as time. A Roman Governor of Britain, Giaus Petronious Arbiter, remarked in the first century AD, "we trained hard but it seemed that every time we

---

* Professor Sir Roy Calne F. R. S. Professor of Surgery, University of Cambridge. Honorary Consultant Addenbrookes Hospital.

were beginning to form teams we would be reorganized. I was to learn later in life that we tend to meet any new situations by reorganizations and what a wonderful method it can be for creating an illusion of progress, while producing confusion, inefficiency and demoralization".

It is in this state that the National Health Service staff finds itself today. With these complex systems of reorganization a NEW CITADEL has arisen within the national Health Service, in which the healers of the sick must live and work and try to attain the objectives which a very long and arduous training could enable them to achieve. This new Citadel has been an amalgam of administration, politics and medicine and to which a strong element of commerce has recently been introduced.

The benefits that the National Health Service has made to the nation must in no way be minimised. Perhaps its most important contribution has been the establishment throughout the entire country of District General Hospitals.

In former years London and Edinburgh were regarded as the medical meccas and to these must be added the provincial University Teaching Hospitals who have produced so many distinguished surgeons and physicians. To obtain the best treatment the patient had to go to one of these centres of excellence which were the keeps of the FIRST CITADEL.

The most important result of the introduction of the National Health Service has been to re-distribute some of the skills and talents from the great Teaching Hospitals to the District General Hospitals, which have been established throughout the length and breadth of the land. It is therefore now possible for patients, wherever they live, to obtain a high standard of treatment in the local District General Hospital, often as good as that which could be obtained in any of the Teaching Schools. This has been the greatest attainment of the National Health Service.

The changes in medicine in the last half century have been profound both in scientific advance and in political involvement.

As time passes, fewer members of the profession survive who have personally experienced the scientific and political changes that have occurred both before and after the advent of the National Health Service.

As one of these few I felt I must put pen to paper and write my personal memoirs of this period of dramatic change. It is perhaps a personal approach which will provide a more human insight into the changes that have occurred and the emotions evoked in the profession at a time of profound change and uncertainty. Inevitably, memoirs require a portrayal of personal background because it is from this that the response of the individual to change is largely determined.

These memoirs begin in the professional scene portrayed by Dr Cronin in *The Citadel* and extend to include contemporary times where a NEW CITADEL has been established under medico-political influence. I have therefore entitled this book, *A Tale of Two Citadels*.

It is the auto-biography of a surgeon who qualified in the provincial city of Belfast, trained in the Teaching Hospitals of London and Edinburgh and then under the new National Health Service started for the first time a Consultant Surgical Service in Darlington, a provincial town which formerly had a hospital service provided by dedicated general practitioners.

This auto-biography starts in peacetime Britain, covers the Second World War and extends over the post-war years to the present day. It covers a period in which scientific advances in medicine have been unique and have provided ever increasing possibilities in the attainment of health and the treatment of disease. It is also a period in which the general population has begun to show an interest in health and the importance of the environment in which they live.

Belfast – A Divided City

IT IS UNDERSTANDABLE that people regard their city of origin with respect, and it is with a certain degree of pride I regard myself as a Belfast man. Four centuries ago Belfast was a simple crossing place on the sandy banks of the river Lagan. It was sited between the last tributary (The Forset) and the river's entrance to the shallow sandy apex of the lough. Belfast (*Beal Feirsde*) has seen many turbulent changes over these four centuries, but in spite of the many upheavals in religion, politics and trade, it has emerged as a Capital city of the Province of Ulster.

Political problems date back to the Elizabethan conquest when the Irish sided with the King of Spain. Economic changes relate to the rise and fall of the cotton and of the linen industry, but the peak of industrial activity was in shipbuilding at the turn of the century. Religious strife has occurred over these centuries, first of all between Protestant and Catholic, and then during the implantation of the Scots in Ulster, between Anglicans and Presbyterians. In the last century the old Protestant and Catholic strife has once again reared its ugly head. Unfortunately, religious difference have developed social and economic overtones which present problems still unsolved.

The politico-religious conflicts continue today and they are accompanied by episodes of terrorism which are now almost a daily occurrence. In spite of these disruptions the ordinary citizens of Ulster try hard and succeed in living a normal life. The incorporation of terrorism in a cloak of normality tends to prevent firm enough measures being taken by Government to eradicate this evil and self perpetuating crime of terrorism.

The citizens of Belfast are in many ways unusual, and it is not surprising that there is an element of Scottish pride in their demeanour and they have an accent which is diagnostic of the city. They are well aware of the great attainments reached in the boom years in the linen industry and of the skill and dedication of the "Queens Island Men" who worked in the shipyards of Harland and Wolfe and who built the *Olympic* and the ill fated *Titanic*, the greatest ships of this era of great ships.

On the opposite side of the river Lagan the engineers of Workman and Clark produced a wide range of smaller but highly specialized container ships which attained a world wide reputation. Even in rope-making and in the tea and tobacco industry the city had its years of glory. Galaghers Green and Galaghers Blue were well known brands of cigarettes in former years.

The Belfast man is characteristically a hard working industrious person who has had little affinity with the Trade Unions, and this in spite of the fact that Trade Unions became overpowerful in mainland Britain before Margaret Thatcher curbed their power. In the face of these virtues it is perhaps unkind to draw the veil on the frailties of the citizens of Belfast and of the Province of Ulster. It is however, a little difficult to ignore the rather narrow minded and often bigoted outlook held so deeply on both religious and political matters, and it is these features that have divided the city of Belfast and indeed the Province of Ulster.

Geographically, the modern city lies in the Lagan valley, bounded to the north by a range of low mountains, the Black Mountain, Divis, Squires Hill, and the craggy outline of Cave Hill. To the south is a range of low hills, the Castlereagh Hills. It was in Cregagh at the foot of these hills where I was born and brought up. This suburb remembers with pride that one of its citizens, a soldier in the famous Ulster Division, won the Victoria Cross in the Battle of the Somme in 1916. The award was posthumous and the name of the McFadzean family is still regarded with awe and reverence by all.

Cregagh was one of the suburbs of Belfast whose development was made possible by the introduction of the electric tramways. These enabled businessmen to commute from home to the city centre. Our home was designed by an architect and built by my father who employed direct labour. As was the custom with suburban houses at this time, each house was detached and made to a different design. This is a very different concept from those estates developed in contemporary Britain where there is such uniformity and dullness in design. The house was named ELSTOW after the village in Bedfordshire where the author John Bunyan was born, and it was in this house where I and my two elder brothers and younger sister were brought up.

2

The Family – Memories of Childhood and School Days

M Y FATHER was a very kindly and industrious man who had a deep religious faith. His reading was largely confined to two books, the Bible and John Bunyan's *Pilgrims Progress*. The Bible he regarded as being divinely and verbally inspired and this was his textbook of Religion. *Pilgrims Progress* was a guide to the practice of a Christian way of life. The characters portrayed by John Bunyan with descriptive names like Mr Worldlywise included all the knowalls that were likely to be encountered in real life. All other books were fictional and to those he applied, with some disparagement, the term 'novel'. It was because of his admiration for Bunyan that he named our house ELSTOW.

He was the eldest of three sons whose father died at the early age of twenty-seven, leaving the upbringing of the family to my grandmother who was a formidable woman with strong Victorian values. At school he showed some artistic talent, and because of this he became a linen designer concerned with the patterns which were the basis of traditional Irish Linen embroidery. The patterns that he drew remained popular for almost half a century before they were replaced by those of more contemporary design. Expanding his activities he set up his own linen business with what would now be described as Thatcherite enterprise. His business survived even the deepest industrial depression after the First World War. His younger brother John died in childhood of "consumption of the bowels", a manifestation of tuberculosis which was so prevalent in Ireland in those days. His youngest brother Charles was encouraged to go into the retail linen business. It was with great interest that I visited my uncle's shop in Portrush and was able to see the beautiful hand embroidery made from my father's designs.

My mother was a clever but retiring and introverted person. Her main occupation was in looking after the family and occasionally entertaining missionary friends of my father who had come from foreign lands. She rarely went out except for our annual two months' holiday which was spent in Portrush on the north coast of County Antrim. She came into her own on these occasions and with my two older brothers Maurice and Owen and my younger sister, Margaret, the Portrush holiday was in institution that seemed endless in time and unlimited in enjoyment.

CHILDHOOD

Childhood memories are often very vivid, and unlike those memories of later life, they retain their clarity and become even more vivid with the passage of the years. It is debatable as to the age at which a child attains the faculty of memory. My own earliest recollection was I believe in infancy, when I was being carried in my mother's arms in our nursery. The nursery looked out over the front garden and across the narrow Knockbreda road to a rather attractive estate known as Glen House. This was the home of a family called Gregg who ran a foundry in Belfast, and who kept their wooded grounds in excellent condition. On this occasion the entire landscape was covered with snow and I believe it was for this reason that my mother wished to show me the landscape. It was quite a dazzling sight with universal whiteness on the ground and the trees of the estate showed the fantastic shapes of snow covered branches.

There was another memory that I believe related to my infancy. For many years I held in my mind an occasion when I was sitting on my father's knee and saw a pier with a bandstand quite near by. I remember being lifted over from my father's to my mother's care. I never was able to identify this scene in all my adolescent years. When I qualified as a doctor at Queen's University, my father and I celebrated the occasion by taking a trip on a pleasure boat that plied from Donegal quay in Belfast to Bangor, which was a small town at the entrance of the lough. We travelled in the steamer which was known locally as the Bangor Boat and as we approached the pier at Bangor, I recognized this long standing,

11

and until then unidentified, mental picture. I mentioned this to my father who assured me that the only time he was on this pier with my mother was just before the onset of the First World War. At that time I would have been just under the age of two.

My other early memories have all had a background of the events of the First World War. While on our annual holiday to Portrush I was walking along a street called Causeway Street, which led out from Portrush to the fantastic rock formation known as the Giant's Causeway I had a startling experience. As I and my brothers were walking along the street there appeared in the sky a great silver object. It was quite a remarkable sight to see this great silver cigar shaped object passing slowly overhead. I was told that it was an airship that was on patrol looking out for German submarines that had been sighted just behind a series of small rock islands just off shore and known as the Skerries.

At this time, also, patrols of bi-planes used to join in the search for submarines. I remember them flying low out over the sandhills that bordered the long stretch of yellow sands that extended from Portrush to the White Rocks. It was to the White Rocks that in later years we used to go to have family picnics. The anticipation of exploring the many caves that extended into the White Rock cliffs was always an intriguing experience for the family. They were explored by candlelight and the candles were frequently extinguished by the dripping water from the roof of the caves. We always had an adequate supply of matches and the exploration of the caves was a highlight of the holiday.

I was to learn in later life that, as the result of these patrols by our airships and our aeroplanes, a German submarine was chased into Loch Swilly where it became stranded by the outgoing tide. The crew I believe were arrested, not by the Navy but by the local police. Airships seemed fated to claim a place in my memory. Very many years later I was to see the ill-fated airship the R101 in flight over Belfast. I was walking along the Knockbreda road on a beautiful moonlit night in 1931 when I heard the sound of strange engines in the sky and then the great silver airship sailed majestically in the moonlight over the Castlereagh Hills on its way to its base at Cardington in Bedfordshire. The R101 and its sister ship, the R100, were part of a dream of luxury in air travel.

The passengers' facilities were spacious and far in advance of those available with aeroplane travel of those days, and were indeed superior to those of first class travel today. Unfortunately, due to technical problems with the highly inflammable hydrogen used in lighter-than-air-flying, this dream of luxury travel was to terminate abruptly in disaster. The R101 caught fire over Beauvais in northern France and was totally destroyed with the loss of all its distinguished passengers,- including the air minister Lord Thompson, who were on their way to India.

My other memory dating back to the First World War was that of Armistice Day. I was playing in the front garden of Elstow when I heard the sounds of factory hooters and the ringing of church bells. My father arrived as was usual at lunchtime and I enquired what all the activity was about. He told me with great relief that the war with Germany was over and that this was the Armistice. I had no real comprehension of the importance of this event but was long to remember the happy expression of relief on my father's face as he gave me this news. But clouds were all too soon to return after the rain, for scarcely had the dust settled after the First World War, when within a brief twenty years the war clouds were gathering again and the whole ghastly process of war was to be repeated all over again.

SCHOOLDAYS

My first school was an infant school about one mile from my home. The solitary school room was in the upper floor of a house in Woodstock Road and was known as Miss Steel's School. It was run by two maiden ladies under whose care I learned to read and write and do simple arithmetic. It was a happy school and though I believe in later years it was threatened with closure by the Department of Education, it could still, with justification, boast that two University Professors were among its former pupils.

My early education was grossly interrupted by the illness of my mother. As I was the youngest boy, to prevent interruption to the education of my elder brothers, I had to stay at home and look after her during her frequent illnesses. She developed episodes of upper abdominal pain and sickness and was diagnosed as suffering form gall stones. No investigations were carried out in the limited facilities available at the time, but in view of subsequent experience, I have no doubt that the clinical diagnosis of our general practitioner was correct.

The treatment of these attacks consisted of the application of poultices to the area of pain. The idea was to produce counter irritation which was thought to relieve the pain and help to clear up the attacks of infection. The family doctor, Dr Adams, of Ravenhill Road, Belfast, instructed me on how to prepare a linseed poultice which consisted of linseed heated up in boiling water and after straining the linseed was placed in a gauze bag. This was applied as hot as tolerable to the affected area. More severe attacks were treated by the use of a mustard poultice which was applied cold but certainly burned the skin.

These applications were very painful and even as a child I suspected that the pain of the application of the poultice was even more severe than the pain of the disease and as such rendered the original pain better or at least more tolerable by comparison. This was my very first experience of managing illness and at this time I never even dreamed that caring for sick people would become, for me, a life's work.

At this time too I was taught the most elementary cooking and realized that there were different times required for the preparation of different foods. As my reading of the clock was not entirely reliable my mother, when bed-ridden, used to make marks on the clock face so that when the two hands came to the appropriate points I would know that the meal was ready.

After I left the infants school the recurrent illnesses of my mother prevented any regular attendance at school and my progress was quite deplorable. Even as I approached the age of ten my subtraction arithmetic was thoroughly unreliable. To rectify this position my parents decided that they could possibly afford to send me to the Royal Academical Institute in Belfast (INST), a school which had a great reputation for academic attainment. So it was to INST that my father took me for interview by the headmaster. He was a austere man with shortish grey hair. His name was Dr R. M. Jones and he was a classical scholar of some distinction. After what seemed to be a long discussion with my father he suddenly turned to me and said, "do you know the first Latin declension?" As both my brothers were already at the school I had been warned of this question and therefore was able to repeat the first declension of

Mensa with such facility that I was immediately admitted to the First Form.

Of the first three years of school I remember almost nothing except for one event which was to give me my first personal foretaste of the work of doctors and of hospitals. I developed enlargement of the tonsils and was seen by our general practitioner, Dr Adams. He felt that the condition should be dealt with and that a surgeon should be consulted.

The procedure involved was just the same as at the present time. The family doctor referred me to the specialist Ear Nose and Throat Surgeon. An appointment was made and my father took me for consultation. I remember this well for we had to go to an address in the rather attractive road know as College Gardens. This was a private road with Georgian houses which looked out over the grounds of the Methodist College, and was the Harley Street of Belfast.

The consultation was simple, no special tests being required. I was advised to have the operation for removal of tonsils at a special hospital in Great Victoria Street.

On an appointed day my mother took me to the hospital and I remember entering this depressing building. Deprived of my breakfast I sat on a hard wooden bench in a corridor, the walls of which were covered with the stark, white, shiny tiles so often seen in old-fashioned public lavatories. There were others waiting, and from time to time a nurse in a long white skirted uniform would swirl into the corridor and escort the next patient for operation.

At last my turn had come and I was taken to the room for operation. I would not described the room as a theatre for it did not possess all the equipment with which in later life I was to become all too familiar.

I was lifted on to the operating table by two nurses who tied a rubber mackintosh round my neck rather like a bib. They stationed themselves on either side of the table each holding my hand. I had thought this contact was to comfort me but was soon to learn that they were the hands of restraint to prevent struggling as the anaesthetic was being administered.

The anaesthetist, Dr Victor Fielding, was well known in Belfast and he used the methods of the time. The term technique is too sophisticated to use in this context. A mask with a balloon attachment known as a Clovers Inhaler was placed over my nose and mouth and by a process of partial suffocation and the inhalation of an anaesthetic agent, ethyl chloride, I was soon asleep for the operation known as tonsil guillotine.

In skilled hands it only takes a few minutes to perform, but I was to learn in later life the dangers of these crude anaesthetic and surgical procedures. I woke up with my face being sponged down with iced water, while a nurse was exhorting me to "spit out"! As soon as I was awake I was taken home by taxi.

This was my personal experience of out-patient surgery, a procedure now elevated in status by the use of the term "day surgery", and advocated by some of our profession perhaps more for medico-political and financial reasons rather than for the attainment of excellence in patient care.

The days which followed were grim indeed. Our family doctor came to see me as I felt ill and was running a temperature. Painful swellings came up in my neck and my parents were informed that my throat had become septic. The only known treatment at that time was to gargle with salt water, a procedure that proved both difficult and painful. It was many weeks before I returned to normal, and the whole experience made a deep impression on me and on my parents.

In the light of my subsequent experience as a surgeon, I wonder what would have happened if I had developed a reactionary haemorrhage the night after operation (which sometimes happens after tonsillectomy) and had no professional nursing or medical supervision, while bleeding was proceeding unnoticed. The thought of this situation is too awful to contemplate and it is this experience and realization that has made the contemporary concept of day care surgery so unattractive to me.

The supervision required for day care surgery, necessitates a much better domiciliary back up which in itself is very expensive on an individual basis. One cannot help but consider that patients are better to remain in hospital over night after many of the procedures for which day surgery is now being recommended. In hospital there is a concentration of skills and facilities to handle many patients together, which must be more economic and efficient than disseminating these resources to individual patients in their own homes. The case for extensive day case surgery is made for financial reasons rather than for attaining excellence in patient care.

It so happened at this time that our family moved temporarily from our home at Cregagh to live nearer the Queen's University where my eldest brother Maurice had been accepted in the Faculty of Medicine and my brother Owen in Divinity. Our home at Elstow was rented to a Monsieur Lasfarge who was the French Consul.

We rented for one year a terraced house in 3 Malone Avenue, Belfast. This belonged to a very religious widow called Mrs. Adams, whose son John had just qualified as a doctor at Queen's University. He left Belfast and set up in a fashionable general practice in Eastbourne where he became more pretentiously known as Dr J. Bodkin Adams. He was well known to our family since we met each year at Portrush on our annual holidays. I remember him quite well reading medical books while sitting on a camp chair on the strand which extended from the harbour at Portrush towards the Black Rocks.

Though Bodkin Adams never made any major contribution to medicine he did attain notoriety in later years in a very famous medico-legal case. He was the Eastbourne general practitioner who in 1956 was accused of murdering one of his wealthy patients by giving an overdose of a sedative drug. He was defended very successfully at the time by Mr Lawrence, the Recorder of Leicester, and was acquitted of this charge. It was to me quite unthinkable that this kindly, highly religious man would ever be guilty of such a crime as murder. Apparently a nurse had made an allegation that led to the charge of murder and such allegations are sometimes similarly made even today.

After a protracted convalescence at Malone Avenue I returned to school but with little enthusiasm until an event altered my entire outlook. It occurred during a winter when a sleighing accident happened on the Castlereagh Hills quite near my home.

A group of children and young people were sleighing down a hill on a farm owned by a John MacCormack. The hill was steep at its upper end but lower down the slope became less marked and the end of the slope was fringed by a row of trees. We all started our sledges on the steep slope but lower down changed direction so that we could avoid the line of trees. Unfortunately, one of our friends, a young girl, failed to make the appropriate change in direction and struck a tree trunk feet first. To my surprise she was rendered unconscious, since I could not see any injury to her head. (I was to learn, as a young doctor, that the accident in which she was involved was likely to result in a fracture of the base of her skull.) We laid her on a sleigh and she was pulled along through the snow to the tram terminus at Cregagh.

I never really got to know what ultimately happened to her but I felt at the time that I only wished I could have done something to help. It was this single experience that kindled in my mind the thought that I would like to be a doctor.

With this secret desire carefully concealed from my family I began to work at school and things were transformed. I enjoyed study but para-doxically also started to take an interest in sport, especially in running. In those days races were measured in yards and it was in the 220 and 440 yards that I had the pleasure of running for the school. Physics and chemistry with advanced mathematics were sufficient to allow me to enter the university in the Faculty of Medicine.

3

Queen's University

THE Queen's University of Ireland was established in 1849 by Queen Victoria to provide a university education available to all citizens. It consisted of three Queen's Colleges, one in Cork, one in Galway and one in Belfast. Since Trinity College, Dublin had long been established, no Queen's College was made in Dublin. In 1907 the system of university education was modified to provide two universities, the National University of Ireland, situated in Dublin with the Royal Colleges of Galway and of Cork attached to it, while the Royal College in Belfast became known as Queen's University.

Queen's University was what is now known as a "red brick" University, but had attained a sound reputation especially in the Medical Faculty. It therefore never occurred to me to attempt to attain an entrance to Oxbridge, but to content myself in diligent study in the university of my home town.

My first impression of university life was one of freedom. Gone was the rigid discipline imposed by school regulation, and one could conduct one's affairs as one thought fit. As time went on it become apparent however, that behaviour still had to be regulated in work and recreation even in the university. Going to university merely changed the discipline of the school, imposed from without, to the discipline of university life imposed from within.

It soon became apparent that the Faculty of Medicine appeared to be much more hard working than the other faculties. Time for other university activities was limited and as the course proceeded study became more and more intense, so that the medical student became more isolated and apart from his fellow university colleagues.

The study of physics and chemistry was very similar to that at school but the subjects of botany and zoology added new interest. Professor "Jimmy" Small, a very distinguished Professor of Botany, appeared to regard medical students as an unavoidable intrusion into his faculty. The study of botany was considered important as the drugs then used therapeutically were derived from plants, of which digitalis, a product of the plant foxglove, and atropine derived from the deadly nightshade are the best known. The drugs of today are of chemical origin, and botany now plays little, if any, role in the training of the medical student of today.

Professor Gregg Wilson, the Professor of Zoology, taught us the facts of the structure and functions of the various species of animals and this he did with a zeal and with an enthusiasm which was almost infectious.

In his lowland Scottish accent he emphasized what he referred to as "the facts of evolution", and we were to learn that in the human embryo there were traces of structures that resembled the kidney of the earth worm and, in later development, the human embryo possessed the urinary system of a frog. It was interesting to know that this latter system was retained, but put to a different function, in the formation of part of the genital system. He also emphasized that there were few surgeons who had not taken out cysts from the human neck which were the embryonic remnants of the gill clefts of fishes, illustrating that man arose from an aquatic species. He was a most stimulating lecturer whose merit I was only fully to appreciate when in later life I took an interest in comparative anatomy.

The realization of these facts of comparative anatomy challenged the religious concepts of the origin of man which were instilled into my mind since earliest childhood, when the origin of man was focused on the Garden of Eden in the pastoral Bible story. The establishment of scientific truth has, over the centuries, produced deep divides between religion, philosophy and the acceptance of the facts of life and of the universe.

The medical student takes the first steps to become a doctor by entering the Departments of Physiology and of Anatomy. Physiology, which is the study of the function of organs of the body, was taught largely on academic grounds with little physical component. By contrast anatomy was a subject of stark reality and involved the study of preserved human corpses. Our introductory lectures were given by Professor Thomas Walmsley the Professor of Anatomy who spoke to us like a kindly philosopher outlining a subject of eternal interest. He emphasized each special point in slow deliberate terms. He insisted that our behaviour in the dissecting room where the preserved human bodies were displayed was to be one of decorum and respect, and we were to appreciate that we had been privileged to be able to study in this way.

Entering the dissecting room for the first time was regarded with apprehension by all medical students, and I shall never forget my first visit.

As I walked up the stairs to the first floor of the Department of Anatomy the smell of formaldehyde, used to preserve the bodies, permeated the whole building and every person in it. On entering the actual room the first vision was of two rows of benches with a central aisle. On each bench was a naked, dark, stained body with the legs sticking up rigidly like the masts of a ghost ship. Between this forest of legs we made our way to the allocated body to begin our first study in anatomy.

It was a grim experience and never to be forgotten, and the smell of preservative seemed to pervade our every activity, and many of us lost appetite and weight.

As first year students we began our studies by dissecting either the arm or the leg, while the second year students were engaged on the same body but studying the more complex anatomy of the head and neck, or of the chest and the abdomen.

It was a very strange sensation to make the first cut into the skin with a scalpel and to touch with forceps the tissues of a dead human body. At first every little piece of tissue seemed to be important, but soon I was able to dissect out the important structures such as arteries, nerves and veins and to study the mechanical function of the joints and the related muscles.

With the passage of time the initial feelings of revulsion were slowly and progressively replaced by a curiosity and interest so that even the all pervading atmosphere of formaldehyde could almost be forgotten.

We were instructed by three doctors who helped us in our studies and who assessed our progress by staged examinations throughout the entire term.

The first of these was the Reader in Anatomy, Dr R. H. Hunter who was next in seniority to the Professor and who was the number two in the department. He was known as "Dickie" Hunter and was a most unusual man. He started life as an artist in Paris and after service in the French Red Cross in World War I, he took up medicine as a mature student and qualified at Queen's at the age of 38. His abilities as a pen and ink artist were outstanding and served him well in his career as an anatomist. Appreciation for his work has been shown by a lecture given by Sir Ian Fraser on the 35th anniversary of the Ulster Surgical Club and by the portrait by Sir James Gunn hung in the Great Hall of the University.

The other two doctors held more junior posts as demonstrators, the senior was Dr Dan Baxter who was to become a career anatomist, and Mr W. M. (Bill) Bassett who was to become a consultant surgeon.

Study in pure anatomy was very intense but by way of wider interest lectures in surgical anatomy were given by a consultant surgeon, a Mr H. P. (Harry) Malcolm.* He was a very dapper figure dressed quite elegantly and in contrast to that of the academic staff in the Department of Anatomy. His lectures were scheduled to start at noon and finish at 1 p.m. Unfortunately, on many occasions, the lectures were prolonged and encroached on the vital lunchtime break. So frequent were these intrusions that some of the students inserted alarm clocks into the chest cavity of skeletons which were hanging from the high ceiling of the lecture theatre from which they were supported by a pulley.

The alarm clocks were timed to go off at intervals of 5 minutes starting at 12.45 p.m. so that towards the end of the lecture these alarms went off in a series. This caused consternation to the lecturer but a great deal of amusement to the students. No sooner had one of the skeletons been lowered down by the lecture attendant, who was called Skillen, to remove the alarm clock when another alarm sounded in the thoracic cage of a different skeleton. Harry Malcolm, the lecturer, was enraged but the students were then assured of a reasonably early lunch break.

I was to become very interested in anatomy and, blessed with a good photographic memory, the subject seemed easy; and indeed this ability

---

* Mr H. P. Malcolm, Consultant Surgeon, Royal Victoria Hospital, Belfast.

was to form a sound basis for my future career as a surgeon. Important values are not always appreciated in prospect but rather in retrospect when years later their crucial value is greatly appreciated, as was the case in my studies in anatomy.

The intensity of work in the first two years in medicine were far and away greater than that in any of the other faculties. This in itself began the isolation process between the medical student and his counterparts in other faculties, as has already been mentioned.

This isolation was to become even more marked when after the second M.B. examination further studies became hospital based. It was perhaps this pressure of work combined with the impact of the study of human disease which made the medical student a student apart. In prospect and in retrospect the second M.B. examination could be regarded as the Beechers Brook of the medical student's course. There were indeed many casualties as the failure rate was high, but those who survived usually passed the subsequent examinations and graduated in the fullness of time.

The time for recreation was very limited and as I had never been very successful on the rugby field, I contented myself with the simple pleasures of running, cycling, and amateur radio. In the late evening after completion of the days study, I used to run from my home to the crossroads where the Knockbreda Road intersected the road to Ballygowan.

This is a point which is now well known by the siting of the Castlereagh Police Interrogation Centre. The running distance was 2 miles which was sufficient to keep me in what we called training. In summer, cycling was the sport of choice and there must be few roads in the Ards peninsula from the Scrabo Tower through Newtown Abbey to the fishing port of Portaferry which were not traversed by my Humber bicycle. In winter, a long and wet season in Ulster, construction and operation of radio equipment, then known as wireless sets was the main interest. The peak of achievement was the making of a five-valve super neutrodyne wireless which was the latest thing in radio receivers. When in operation the five brightly lighted valves provided enough illumination and indeed enough heat to make comfortable the long night sessions of searching for foreign stations. There were five tuned circuits, each with three controls, which had to be adjusted individually to get the best results.

On one occasion my brother Maurice and I achieved a very unusual success when we received a transatlantic signal on long waves from Miami Beach. We heard the announcer say, "this is Miami Beach (WIOD) wonderful isle of my dreams", and then was played the theme song of the station *Long Long Ago*. In those days transatlantic reception was quite exceptional and we were both very pleased.

Sadly, as study became more intense, there was little time for these midnight adventures, and with the advancement of short wave wireless telegraphy such sessions became unnecessary.

4

The Medical Student in Hospital

COMPLETION of the second M.B. examination and mastery of the basic sciences of physiology, anatomy and bio-chemistry enables the medical student to continue the arduous course on the way to becoming a doctor. It is at this stage that he takes the first steps of instruction in clinical medicine, where teaching takes place in the hospitals which are the classrooms of clinical medicine.

Leaving the university precincts and entering hospital is like pulling aside the curtains and entering into the full world stage of real life and people. It is at the same time exciting and yet intimidating and many successful academic students are overcome by its potentialities and in later life find comfort in reclusive academicy.

A hospital is a unique institution, and is unlike a factory, office or store. It combines the accommodation of a hotel, the catering of a restaurant, and the laboratory of a scientific institution. It contains a wide range of electronic equipment in an ever increasing and accelerating field of electro-physical science and technology.

To add to the complexity the hospital staff is drawn from a wide social spectrum of people, from the hospital cleaner through the clerical, nursing and medical staff to the esoteric intellect of some academic genius. It is because of these peculiar features of hospital life and structure that reports commissioned by governments on the running of hospitals have proved of such limited value. Such reports submitted by successful industrialists have proved wanting and often harmful, in that they have extrapolated ideas and methods from industry which are alien to medicine.* These reports are unsuitable and indeed inappropriate for hospitals and for their special needs.[1, 2]

My first attendance at hospital was at The Royal an affectionate term used for the Royal Victoria Hospital in Grosvenor Road, Belfast. Travelling to hospital was by tram from my home near the Cregagh terminus to Castle Junction, and then a change of tram to reach the hospital. As the tram clattered and rocked down the Woodstock Road I had many thoughts and fears. To visit hospital as a patient causes anxiety lest the consultation reveals serious disease, while to visit a sick friend evokes thoughts of sympathy and concern.

To go to hospital as a medical student is a very different matter. It provides the first glimpse of what life as a doctor will be like, a prospect that is viewed with a mixture of anticipation and of apprehension. Anticipation of the excitement of entering this new and unknown world of medicine and all the interest that it may provide, but coupled with feelings of apprehension that one might fail intellectually or emotionally to attain the standards demanded by this the most arduous of the professions.

The tram stopped outside the Royal Victoria Hospital and I met many of my student friends who were at the entrance to the hospital.

The formalities of registration as a first year clinical student were soon complete. The group was quite small and was divided into three sections, medical, surgical and out-patients, so that each hospital department had its allocation of attached students.

Some of my friends that were at school at St. Malachys College which was a Roman Catholic School, went to the Mater Informorum Hospital, a hospital founded by a catholic order, but those of us who were educated at INST, Campbell College and other protestant schools, became medical students at the Royal Victoria Hospital. Though I did not consciously recognize it at the time this was a type of religious segregation which was a feature so regrettable in much of Ulster life.

My first impression of hospitals was one of constant activity of nurses, doctors and patients. In the corridors the staff walked with a sense of purpose and of unhurried urgency. The red dresses and well laundered

---

* The Salmon Report on nursing, The Griffiths Report on hospital administration.

white aprons of the nurse's uniforms were an outstanding feature. One realized that slight differences in the cap or the uniform indicated a difference of nursing rank or seniority.

The medical staff too had their different modes of dress. The resident house doctors wore long white coats, while the students wore short white coats, which distinguished them from those who were qualified doctors. When a student qualified he gave up his short white coat and was able to wear a long coat. Some who became overbearing because of this transition were said to be suffering from "long coatitis" a disease that soon cured itself with increasing experience.

Administrators were seldom, if ever, seen and yet the hospital seemed to run with smooth efficiency and there were very many less lay staff than are seen in a hospital of today.

Another feature was the outstanding cleanliness of the entire building. The floors were constantly being scrubbed by hand, and the charwoman kneeling on the floor was upset if we, as students, walked on the wet floor. The atmosphere was permeated by the smell of antiseptic which was a measure of the care being taken to avoid infection in this pre-antibiotic era, because infection was a major risk to the patient.

It is perhaps true to say that the high standards of hygiene in this antiseptic era are not attained in today's hospitals where infection is so easily treated by antibiotics and poses a much smaller threat to patient welfare.

In the medical wards the outstanding event was the consultants round, which took place once or twice a week. The consultant, his assistant and the house staff saw and discussed every patient in the ward. The ward sister was present on every occasion. The house physicians and the more senior medical students were at the front of all this conclave, but the first year clinical students were very much at the back. This had the advantage that questions from the consultant were addressed to the more senior students, but had the disadvantage that the view of events and of the patient was somewhat impaired.

In the surgical wards the duty of attending the Grand Round was equally important but there were in addition the duties associated with the operating theatre which is the nucleus of the surgical discipline. Seeing my first operation was quite an experience and one that I shall never forget. It was the most dramatic point in my undergraduate career.

Each surgical unit in the Royal Victoria Hospital had a male and female ward with one operating theatre attached to the unit. The most prestigious of the theatres was at Wards 19 and 20 where there was an overhead observers gallery. The other six operating theatres had little observer accommodation and this was on the ground floor. I remember climbing up the stairs to reach the dimly lit gallery and crept slowly forwards to look down from the gallery on the scene below. It was a most remarkable sight.

The surgeon and his assistants, all wearing masks and hoods, were clad in white gowns and were clustered on either side of the operating table. The anaesthetist was giving a chloroform and ether anaesthetic on an open mask and the smell of this anaesthetic mixture rose up into the students gallery. The focal point was the operating field which was illuminated with an intense white light from a sialitic lamp which quite remarkably cast no shadows on the site of operation. The breathing movements of the patient could be seen and this added to an element of reality and drama. At the bottom end of the operating table there was a trolley with groups of instruments laid out neatly in a special order. The theatre sister, a key person in the drama, slapped into the hand of the surgeon the required instrument at just the right time.

The operation to be performed was a major one for the removal of a gall bladder which was diseased and full of stones. Perhaps the most disturbing feature of the operation was the skin incision and the bleeding caused by the surgeon's scalpel, and it was difficult to believe that this was being done on a live human being. The individual bleeding points were caught in forceps and tied with catgut and soon the bleeding stopped.

Once the initial shock was over and the operation was underway it became a very interesting technical exercise, each manoeuvre being carried out with experienced precision. The atmosphere in the operating theatre depended on the surgeon who set the tempo for the entire surgical stage. At certain times the atmosphere became tense and there was absolute silence as some critical manoeuvre was carried out but at other times there was a feeling of ease and of relaxation. Once the gall bladder had been removed the wound was closed in a routine manner, a dressing was applied and the great drama was over.

I realized how appropriate was the term operating theatre for indeed the operation resembled a drama in which each actor played his special part. The term operating rooms now used so commonly in the United States is more appropriate to a factory or workshop. It is completely inappropriate to use the word room to an operative scene where the knowledge, skills and experience of each member of the team combine with individual personalities to carry out with precision, what is in fact a very skilled surgical drama.

Added to the student's experience in the ward and the operating theatre the third phase of student instruction was concerned with out-patients. The teaching in hospital was at routine medical, surgical or gynaecological out-patient clinics as well as in the casualty departments where accidents and emergencies were dealt with.

The out-patient clinics were where the patients had their first contact with the hospital services. Each patient had a letter of referral from his own family doctor to the specialist concerned. As students we learned how to obtain an accurate clinical history from the patient, give due consideration to his complaints and to build up from these the possible or likely causes of his trouble. Many patients were over anxious and talkative and required skilled restraint while others overcome with fear were silent and withdrawn and required encouragement to present their problems. Even the rare malingerer could be detected by careful taking of the clinical history and this, without the use of any coercion or force. History taking was an exercise in detection.

Though routine pathological, bio-chemical and X-ray examinations were available, these were much less sophisticated that those of the present day. It was this point that made history taking and careful physical examination of paramount importance in arriving at an accurate diagnosis. The use of the most modern scanning technique makes diag-nosis much easier and more precise than in former years.

Each clinic brought its special highlights of interest. Every patient and their disease was different and therefore presented a series of pictures which the student could learn to recognize and to store in his mind

29

rather like a memory scrap book. As time went on the various conditions fell into groups and the mental scrap book became more organized and formed the basis of clinical experience.

Not only were the various diseases of great interest but the patients themselves presented many problems. It was then that I learned that it is just as important what patient has the disease, as what disease the patient has. In those days specialization was not as developed as it is today, so that each clinic presented a very wide range of conditions.

There was however, one special clinic that dealt with venereal diseases, a subject which was well known but too indelicate to discuss in public. The two major diseases then presenting were those of syphilis and of gonorrhoea both of which had increased in frequency since the First World War.

Syphilis was by far the more serious in that in the third stage of the disease the heart and major arterial vessels could be affected seriously and it was indeed sad to see some young ex-serviceman in his thirties die of cardiac problems arising from venereal disease. The other major problem in the syphilitic patient was paralysis of the legs, sometimes associated with madness. Though treatment was available for the condition it was not nearly so effective as that available at the present day.

Gonorrhoea was less of a threat but did have its complications in that many patients developed narrowing of the urinary passage and had difficulty in passing water. Those cases that had developed this urinary obstruction were dealt with at a special clinic which was held on a Sunday morning and which was rather humorously called The Bible Class.

At this clinic the narrowed passage was stretched up by dilator and the skill of urethral dilatation varied with the doctor on duty. If he was particularly good and caused the patients no pain the news seemed to spread widely and the clinic became overwhelmed with increasing numbers. On the other hand if the first patients were hurt then the whole clinic seemed to vanish. It was quite obvious that a local information service was in operation and this was called by the students, The Gonorrhoea Club.

The casualty department was never short of excitement and drama. In a large town during the day there was a constant stream of industrial and road accidents. On one occasion I had the sad experience of seeing one of my colleagues whose name was Moffat brought in with a fracture of the skull. The front wheel of his motor cycle had caught in the deep ruts of the tram lines and he was thrown off the cycle and his head had struck the ground. At this time crash helmets were only used in motor cycle races and were not in civilian use. Unfortunately, he died twelve hours after admission, as neurosurgical intervention for brain damage was seldom practised in those days.

One of the most remarkable features of these years of hospital clinical study was that they were continuous without the interruption of annual holidays. The summer holidays of university study were gone and one year passed into the next without punctuation and the medical student arrived at a new stage in his development.

It was at this time in his fourth year of study that he was required to live in hospital for a period of about six weeks in the medical unit and a similar period in the surgical wards. During this period the student did the work of a house surgeon but under very strict supervision. This was a most valuable period of development and instruction and it was an arrangement for which the medical school of Queen's University can take great credit as this concept of a student in residence was far in advance of its time.

In pre-war years after a student had passed his final M.B. examination, he could take up a junior appointment in hospital or even go into general practice without having the vital experience of being a resident under supervision in hospital. This position was corrected in the post-war years in other medical schools where the graduate in medicine has to carry out a fixed period in hospital practice in a recognized appointment before he can be registered as a fully qualified medical practitioner. Queen's University had, in principle, introduced this system before it was legally required.

These medical students in residence were called PUPS and I did my routine three months in medicine and in surgery in the Royal Victoria Hospital in Belfast. In medicine I worked in the wards of a consultant physician called Robert (Bertie) Marshall and in surgery I worked in the wards of Professor P. T. Crymble, the Professor of Surgery at Queen's University.

Dr Marshall was, in my view, a perfect physician and looked the part.

31

He had a special interest in cardiac disease and was regarded as the leading cardiologist in Ulster. He had a great admiration for French physicians and quoted widely from their works, especially from the work of Laennec, who was the inventor of the stethoscope. As would be expected his wards (Wards 5 & 6) were full of patients suffering from a wide variety of cardiac complaints. Many were in cardiac failure and because of poor oxygenation and impaired blood supply to the brain the patients used to get nightmares and scream out in their sleep which I found very disturbing on my night rounds. Other than regulating cardiac rhythm with digitalis there was little that could be done to alleviate the sufferings of these cardiac cripples.

It was at this time that I first used with pride my newly acquired stethoscope. These instruments held a mystical power with patients, and enormously increased the status of the user: stethoscopes and doctors were inextricably linked.

Under Bertie Marshall's tuition we listened and we soon learned the normal sounds and the abnormal heart sounds which were called murmurs. These indicated that the various valve mechanisms of the heart were not working properly and with great clarity Bertie Marshall would described the murmurs in words and sounds—from the soft systolic blowing murmur associated with incompetence of the mitral valve and the rough rumbling ingravescent murmur of more serious valvular disease.

Using my experience with wireless sets I was able to construct a radio instrument which would amplify the cardiac sounds which could be heard through the loudspeaker of my super neutrodine amplifier set. This gave me much interest but caused some annoyance to the non-medical members of the family, who were disturbed by the constant sound of "Lub Dub", the sound of a normal heart beat.

It was at this time, too, that I first encountered that fascinating condition known as "night nurses palsy". During the night ward round each patient was visited by the house physician,the pupil in residence and the night superintendent.

The night superintendent was Sister Dynes, a formidable character feared by all, but in particular by the nurses. She was known as Diana as a sign of fear rather than of affection. When she entered the ward the nurses stood instantly to attention like soldiers in the Brigade of Guards.

The nurse on night duty used to sit in the middle of the ward, her desk lighted by the downward beams of a shaded lamp. The scene was reminiscent of Scutari and Florence Nightingale of Crimean war fame.

On one particular occasion the house physician and I entered the ward with Diana and approached the nurse who was sitting under the shaded light in the middle of the ward. She looked at us with understanding eyes but to my astonishment remained unmoved in her chair. Diana took the night report from under her hands, looked at it thoroughly and then proceeded to the ward next door. A moment or two later the nurse concerned came rushing in, pale and in terror. She explained that though she saw us clearly she was completely unable to move and was profuse in her apologies for not standing up.

To my surprise Diana was completely sympathetic and explained to us that this was a condition known as "night nurses palsy" and was often associated with over fatigue. It is a condition now more clearly recognized as a type of narcolepsy.

In the medical wards interest was indeed great, but successful medical treatment rare. It was this failure of medicine that was to turn my mind to other methods of treatment.

I entered the surgical ward as a pupil to Professor P. T. Crymble who was Professor of Surgery at the University. I was very impressed with the name for I had noted that Crymble had been mentioned in Gray's Anatomy, the famous textbook which I had studied for my second M.B. examination. I had a great reverence for text books and a great respect for the names of doctors contained therein. It was therefore with an attitude of awe that I began my work in Crymble's ward.

I found that the whole atmosphere on the surgical ward was one of dramatic activity and very different from the quiet and peaceful atmosphere prevailing in a medical ward. In addition to the routine ward duties I had to learn how to scrub up and to put on sterile masks, gowns and gloves which would enable me to assist at operations.

At first I was relegated to second assistant but during the sickness of the house surgeon, a Dr W. M. Loughridge, I was allowed to become first assistant to the Professor. This was a difficult task for I found that in spite of his obvious operative skills he had an intention tremor and his hand shook as he was operating and this I found to be disturbing. It seemed to be accepted that if anything went wrong the blame immediately fell on the assistant who was appropriately admonished or even abused.

For the more major procedures one of the junior consultant surgeons would be asked to be first assistant and I was relegated to second or even third assistant.

On one occasion when the professor was doing a particularly major case the junior consultant, a Mr James Loughridge* was the first assistant. All sorts of problems were encountered and the atmosphere was tense. As usual the assistant was being blamed for all the problems and Mr Loughridge was having a bad time when suddenly the professor realized his assistant was in fact a consultant colleague. The professor looked round the theatre and spotted me as the third assistant who was taking no part whatever in the procedure, when he exploded, "McKeown, it is all your fault".

In the years between the First and Second World Wars there was a great increase in the number of patients suffering from indigestion due to duodenal ulcer. Professor Crymble had a special interest in this disease and in its surgical treatment. In this he followed the teaching of Sir Berkley Moynihan who was a world leader in this field. Moynihan was the Senior Surgeon at the Leeds General Infirmary and was a surgical giant of world renown. In later life he was elevated to the peerage and formed with Professor Grey Turner of Newcastle, a famous surgical association known as the Association of Surgeons of Great Britain and Ireland. More particularly he formed a group of the more élite and distinguished provincial surgeons called the Moynihan Surgical Club, with an inscription on its distinguished crest, "Without Frontiers". It was, and still is, the highest ambition of provincial surgeons to be elected to this august body.

The influence of Moynihan in the surgical treatment of duodenal ulcer was immense. He advocated an operation called gastro-enterostomy in which the digestive acid juices from the stomach were diverted so that they did not pass over the inflamed ulcerated area in the duodenum and therefore allowed the ulcer to heal. This "short circuit" operation was

---

* Mr James Loughridge, B.Sc, F.R.C.S., Consultant Surgeon, Royal Victoria Hospital

considered in England and in the United States of America, to be the operation of choice in the two decades between the world wars. This view was not shared by European surgeons, especially those in Vienna who preferred to remove part of the stomach (partial gastrectomy).

But surgical success was not always assured following this operation and complications did occur. I remember very clearly one middle-aged man, with whom I had become very friendly while he was under treatment, who developed post operative complications that were to prove fatal. He was operated on and at first all seemed to go well, but soon after operation he began to vomit, and in spite of all the measures taken he continued to vomit and ten days later he died in coma. The condition was known as "cyclical vomiting" and at that time the causation was obscure.

It was immensely disturbing, having spoken to this patient so often in the ward, to go to the post-mortem room and quite unexpectedly to see an examination carried out on this very patient who had become quite a friend. I was very surprised to find that there was no visible cause of death and for the first time realized that a patient could die of biochemical changes in the blood in the absence of any structural and visible abnormality.

It was at this time when working in hospital, when still a teenager, that I was faced for the first time with death. Strangely enough I could accept more easily death due to an accident as in the case of my friend Moffat, or the inevitability of death due to old age, but for a younger person to die of disease seemed to me to be a very different matter. One hoped that with advancing knowledge and skills that this type of death due to chemical changes in the body could be avoided, a hope that has now been realized.

Inevitably, the deceased was the central focus of the drama, but like the ripples on a pond, the effects could spread far and wide and many people become involved in the grief. Not even the religious belief and the prospects of resurrection can calm the qualms of personal bereavement. However, in the busy life in hospital such memories pass to the background of one's mind, and the brain, like a good librarian, retains what it thinks is valuable and discards what is less important.

In visits to other hospitals those to the Fever Hospital and to the then Lunatic Asylum in Purtysburn made the most impact. At the Fever Hospital we saw all the common fevers such as measles and mumps but also saw many case of tuberculosis which were housed in a special sanatorium. At this time, in the pre-antibiotic era, tuberculosis was one of the most serious threats to the health of children and young adults. Whether in the glandular form or in the form of pulmonary (lung) disease its impact was great and there was no drug effective in the treatment. It was pathetic to see young people, often strangely beautiful, fade away slowly in this disease which was appropriately called "consumption".

In lunacy and mental disease the outlook was equally gloomy. From the depressive patient gazing out blankly from a seat in the corner of the ward, to the patient suffering from acute mania there were all grades and conditions. During one particular ward round we were escorted by the medical officer and by a "special patient". This person was describing the various patients in each ward and when he approached a man who had delusions of grandeur he said, "this man thinks he is Napoleon". Then he went on to say, "this man's a fool for how can he be Napoleon when I am". It is of interest to note that in the last half century immense advances have been made in the treatment of psychiatric disease and one will never return to the depressing sights which were seen in the wards at Purtysburn Asylum.

Each day brought new experience and knowledge so that there was never any problem of boredom or idleness, and the three years of clinical tuition passed very quickly. It was a time of shared experience and of the formation of friendships, many of which became lifelong and of great value.

In the spring of 1935 the spectre of the final examination began to loom on the horizon like a great cloud. In the Faculties of Arts, Law, Science or Commerce the final examination confers a single degree at the end of a three year course. In medicine the position is different and the course lasts for five years. In the disciplines of medicine and surgery each has its own Bachelor degree, the M.B. and the B.Ch. In Ireland, because of the former historical problems with obstetrics, special attention is given to midwifery and this is recognized with the award of a separate degree, the B.A.O., in Obstetrics and Gynaecology. There are, therefore, three degrees awarded on successful graduation in medicine.

The final examination was indeed a long and exhausting process, as each examination had a written, clinical and oral section in each of the individual specialities. It resembled an academic marathon race and survival was to the fittest. All competitors were exhausted at the end of the examination.

Though the second M.B. examination was regarded as the most difficult to pass, it was only one of a series of hurdles to be surmounted. The final examination was however different in that it was the last and marked the end of undergraduate days.

5

Graduation

WHEN the time arrived for the publication of the graduate list we all assembled in the main hall at the Queen's University to hear the results. The joy of success and the disappointment of failure was written on each face. I could hardly believe the results when I heard my name included, and I checked and re-checked to make sure that my name was actually on the list. Congratulations and commiserations were the order of the day and, as time went on, the crowd slowly melted away and the hall became empty.

I lingered on in disbelief at having passed the final examination and felt like the Guest in the song, *Oft in the Stilly Night* where "the guests had fled, the garlands dead and all but he departed". It is strange to relate that after five long years of studies to attain the degree in medicine there was mingled with the elation of success a strange feeling of anti-climax now that the long ordeal was over.

Celebrations of graduation were simple and enjoyable. My father took me on a trip on Belfast Loch where I was able to recall the infantile memories of the pier at Bangor. My other celebration was to take a girlfriend to whom I subsequently became engaged, for a picnic to Helens Bay. It was glorious weather and we planned the future. A fine artist, Sarah subsequently painted a picture of *Le Quai Vert* (The Green Quay) at Brugge, to celebrate this occasion.

It was at this time that I first realized that my ambitions to be a doctor had been fulfilled. I was in later life to realize that obtaining the title "Doctor" was easier than reverting to the title of "Mr" on gaining the Fellowship of the Royal College of Surgeons. The first five years of the academic life of a surgeon are devoted to getting the title "doctor" and the next five years in getting rid of it.*

Graduation is a landmark in any academic career. The ceremony, enriched by the various gowns and hoods of the different degrees and faculties, is a most colourful occasion. It is the academic equivalent of the pageantry of state occasions for which Britain is so famous. In the thronging crowd the isolation of the medical student seemed to disappear and he became once again part of the greater academic body, while honorary degrees awarded to outstanding persons broadened the interest outside the university campus.

Graduation was for me a time for reflection, for taking stock and for planning. On reflection I felt that we at Queen's University had had a sound medical education. Under Professor Thomson† medical instruction was sound if not brilliant. In obstetrics and gynaecology Professor C. G. Lowry was well known and respected while Professor P. T. Crymble was one of a group of sound surgeons.

In the light of subsequent experience as a consultant surgeon it is perhaps possible to make a more informed assessment of the merits of the Belfast Surgical School. The most brilliant surgeon was "Barney" Purse who never seemed to gain the recognition which he deserved.

There was one lone eccentric senior surgeon called "Pa" Kirk whose initials I never really knew. He never attained a Fellowship of any of the Royal Colleges of Surgeons as apparently he failed at his first attempt at the examination and refused to sit again. Among many other strange ideas, he had however, some insight into the importance of immunity in surgical conditions.

In the days before the discovery of sulphonamides and penicillin, a patient's own immunity was the only defence against infection. Kirk felt that an animal, especially an old one, that had survived must have in its body fluids some substances which were protective. He therefore gave his patients "normal horse serum" as a means of prevention and treatment of infection.

---

* The use of the term "Mister" dates back to the days of the barber Surgeons, when each surgeon had an apprentice. There was therefore a "Master" and an apprentice but with the passage of time "Master" changed into "Mister".
† Prof. W. W. D. Thomson, Professor of Medicine, Queen's University, Belfast.

Modern developments now emphasize the importance of the immune response, not only in infective but also in malignant conditions as pointed out by Professor P. J. Guillou and also by the author.[3, 4] In this respect "Pa" Kirk was perhaps well in advance of his time.

The most orthodox surgeon was Mr S. T. Irwin who in later life was awarded a Knighthood for his services to surgery in Belfast.

It would seem, however, that Belfast surgery was in a state of limbo following the passing of Andrew Fullerton who was Professor of Surgery.

Fullerton had established a world wide reputation in surgery and introduced into the Royal Victoria Hospital many of the concepts and procedures that he had encountered in America while in the clinic of the great Harvey Cushing. Fullerton was the first to insist that surgeons operating at the hospital should be appropriately dressed in gowns, masks and gloves. His contributions to urology (disease of the urinary system) was well known and especially the operation for removal of the prostate gland.

Of the junior surgeons, two were of special notice. The first was J. S. Loughridge[*] and the second Ian Fraser.[†] James Loughridge took a degree in physiology (the study of normal organ function) before qualifying in medicine and becoming a Fellow of the Royal College of Surgeons of England. His physiological approach was apparent in all his thinking and in the teaching of medical students. He was a quiet self-effacing and retiring personality whose surgical judgement was first class and his operative technique safe and sound. The highest compliment that can be paid to him was that his colleagues were happy to be under his skilled care.

Ian Fraser was, on the other hand, extroverted and of great charm. He was an assistant to the great Andrew Fullerton and he absorbed his surgical culture. As a Brigadier in the Royal Army Medical Corps he did much work in the use of penicillin in preventing wound infection in war casualties. Knighted for his services to surgery the honours conferred on him are too numerous to mention. Blessed with good health he is still a

---

[*] J. S. Loughbridge, B.Sc., M.D., F.R.C.S. Eng
Consultant Surgeon, Royal Victoria Hospital
[†] Sir Ian Fraser, D.S.O., O.B.E., D.L., L.L.D., F.R.C.S., F.R.C.S.I.
Consultant Surgeon, Royal Victoria Hospital

distinguished father figure of British Surgery and his memoirs are a delight to read.[5]

In taking stock of the situation in Belfast I felt that I should follow the lead of my eldest brother Maurice who graduated in medicine and had gone to work in London. Though my home life was happy there were some indefinable features in the attitudes of the people in Ulster that gave me a feeling of constraint. Political and religious feelings were strongly entrenched and bigotry ran deep.

At this stage I could not visualize myself continuing to a career in Belfast while the lure of London and its reputed excellence provided an alternative which was so attractive. I decided to try to gain my first junior hospital appointment in the metropolis.

By good fortune I was short listed for an appointment at the King Edward Memorial Hospital in Ealing, and set off for London with no money and no assurance whatever of success. In 1935 air travel was in its infancy and ship and train were the modes of transport. I well remember going with my parents and Sarah to the Donegal quay to embark on my journey to England. Along the quayside below the Queen's Bridge there were the familiar line of cross channel steamers going to Glasgow, Ardrossan, Ayr, Heysham and Liverpool. It was with sadness that I watched my parents with Sarah on the quayside as the Liverpool boat pulled out into the river and headed out into Belfast Lough.

Sleep did not come easily and I had no difficulty in catching the 8 a.m. train from the Lime Street Station in Liverpool to London Euston.

I was quite amazed by the speed of train travel in England. When I was a boy the family used to travel from Belfast from the York Street terminus of the London, Midland and Scottish Railway to Portrush for our annual holiday. The journey of about sixty miles took some two hours but the journey's end was rewarded by greetings from the head porters of various Portrush Hotels who called out the names of their hotels and escorted us either by horse drawn carriage or by Irish side car. Though the journey of some 150 miles from Liverpool to London took about the same time as that to Portrush the welcome at Euston was very different.

A taxi took me to a modest hotel in 2 Cartwright Gardens in Bloomsbury where I was to stay until I went for interview the following day.

From the Russell Square underground station I successfully managed on my first experience of the underground to change to the Central London line at Holborn and to arrive safely at Ealing Broadway. The walk through the Broadway and along the tree-lined Mattock Lane to the King Edward Memorial Hospital was a pleasant but pensive journey. I wondered if a stranger from Belfast would have a chance of being appointed in the face of opposition from the young graduates of London University.

To my astonishment and joy I was appointed to the post of House Physician, House Surgeon and Casualty Officer at the hospital. Thus started my career in medicine.

6

Cronin's Citadel

EALING was a quiet and peaceful suburb of Victorian houses enhanced by the presence of the famous common. The population was middle class and middle-aged. The hospital was situated in a quiet road which ran parallel to what used to be the old road from London to Oxford. Having lived in as a medical student in the Royal Victoria Hospital made it easier for me to settle in my first resident hospital appointment. The hospital was one of a great number of hospitals throughout the land which were built to commemorate the Monarch or to pay tribute to those who served and died in the First World War.

My first appointment was, therefore, as House Surgeon at a hospital that was built to commemorate the reign of King Edward VII.

My final appointment fifteen years later as Senior Consultant Surgeon in Darlington was to a hospital commemorating the dead of the First World War. In the Darlington Memorial Hospital there is a plaque to commemorate the most decorated family in the British Army, known as the "Bradford Boys" or the "Fighting Bradfords". This year is the 100th anniversary of the birth of Ronald Bradford, who was the senior of four brothers, three of whom were killed in the first World War. Ronald won the V.C. and the M.C. and was the youngest ever Brigadier-General in the British Army, but was killed at the age of twenty-five. His brother George was in the Navy and won the V.C. for a daring exploit at Zeebrugge and died at the age of thirty-one. The third family casualty of the war was James who won the Military Cross at the Somme but died of his wounds at the age of twenty-eight. Only one of the four brothers, Thomas, was to survive. He won the Distinguished Service Order and returned to his home in Co. Durham to live a full life to the age of eighty.

The resident medical staff in hospital are in various grades from house surgeons and house physicians up to the grade of senior resident medical/surgical officer. The senior resident surgical officer at the King Edward Memorial Hospital was older than the other residents as he had served as a soldier in the First World War and had qualified in medicine after his discharge from the army in 1918. He was, by coincidence, a graduate of Queen's University in Belfast and a Fellow of the Royal College of Surgeons of Ireland. It was Leslie Ross who briefed me in my duties in this my first appointment.

The consultant staff of the hospital were based in Harley Street or in its sister professional addresses in Wimpole Street and in Devonshire Place. The consultants were the most distinguished members of our profession who held honorary appointments in the great London Teaching Hospitals. They were held in great respect and even in awe when they arrived for their weekly visit to the hospital. It was my duty to meet them as their Rolls Royces pulled up at the hospital and to assist them in every way until their session of work was complete and they returned to their consulting rooms in the West End. Their work in the hospital was entirely honorary and unpaid but carried very considerable status, and acted as an entry into private practice.

Except for emergency admissions which were either arranged by direct contact between the general practitioner and the resident medical staff, or brought into hospital by ambulance from accidents in the street, cases were referred from their general practitioners to the consultants just the same as at the present day.

The hospital service was free to all those who were unable to pay, but patients who were better off were asked to make a donation to the hospital. This financial detail was arranged by the lady almoner who was a person of great tact, sympathy and insight. For the more major and serious problems reference was made to the consultant at his teaching hospital rather than at the local voluntary hospital, where facilities were limited compared with those available at the great London Teaching Schools.

There was much merit in this system because the higher the standard of medical skill and care, the more sought after was the consultant who provided the best service. Those patients who wished to be treated privately could have the alternatives of treatment at a private hospital such as the London Clinic, in the private wing of the hospital, or in one of the many nursing homes that existed at this time. The whole system was an incentive to attain the highest skills in all patient care.

There were, however, occasions when patients would see their consultants in Harley Street but were unable to afford the full cost of private treatment, especially when it involved surgical operation. Frequently such patients, having been seen in private consultation, were admitted to the local hospital, and on occasions appeared to be given priority over other patients. There were some people who considered this morally wrong and indeed the whole system was brought into question by Dr Cronin in his book, *The Citadel*. He regarded the whole consultative structure as a means of perpetuating professional self interest.

In actual fact the system had close parallels with that operating in legal practice where a solicitor calls in a counsel to give a consultative opinion, a system which is successfully in operation to the present day.

Perhaps the most remarkable feature about hospital work at this time was the close association between the doctors and the nurses. They worked as one team and neither sought nor aspired to independence. The nurses educative and training requirements were taken care of by the Sister Tutor supported by lectures by the doctors and the consultants on the staff of the hospital. It was an ideal system of co-operation which had great medical and political advantages.

Regrettably, this has disappeared in the developments in the post-war period when the nursing profession has sought independence but has perhaps inherited isolation and loss of status. The most recent concept of "consultant nurses" is perhaps an attempt to replace this loss.

The administrative staff were few and friendly. They saw their role as one of helping the medical staff so that the patient, the doctor and the nurse would meet in ideal circumstances. Administration and finance was secondary in importance to the central focus of the patient and his medical need. There was no attempt to fit the nursing and medical staff into an administrative structure as is being attempted today with its consequent disastrous results on the medical and nursing staff morale and on those who bear the ultimate responsibility for patient care.

My duties in the King Edward Hospital started in the medical wards where I was House Physician to Dr A. E. Clarke Kennedy. He was a tall man of great intellect who was consultant physician at the London Hospital and who subsequently became Professor of Medicine at Cambridge and was a fellow of Corpus Christi College.

The work was of a broader spectrum than that in Belfast where I worked in what was primarily a cardiac ward. As before, I found medicine of great intellectual interest but the results of treatment were disappointing.

Because of the pressure on the medical beds, those patients who became chronically ill were transferred to one of the hospitals run by the local authorities where there were more beds available. These hospitals, run by the local authorities of London and of Middlesex were of a different type. The medical staff were full time and formed a salaried service in various grades under the direction of a medical superintendent who ran the hospital. They were completely overshadowed by the excellence of the London Teaching Consultants; and the London County Council and the Middlesex County Council Hospitals provided a second tier service. It is feared by many in the profession today that a similar situation has now arisen as the result of the Government's recent proposals.

There were, however, two outstanding surgeons who attained international reputation while working in the County Council Hospitals. The first was Norman Tanner, the surgeon at St. James's Hospital in Balham whose work in gastric surgery and the treatment of peptic ulcer was to become world renowned, and whose trainees are now consultants in Britain and throughout the world. The second was Ivor Lewis, the surgeon at the Central Middlesex Hospital whose contribution to the treatment of cancer of the oesophagus was outstanding. The fact that there is an operation known as the Lewis-Tanner procedure is tribute to the skills of these two brilliant surgeons.

The six months of work in the medical ward was followed by a similar period in the surgical unit which was combined with occasional duties in the Casualty Department. I worked mainly with Mr C. P. Wilson who was a consultant at the Middlesex Hospital and who diligently taught me how to remove tonsils by dissection rather than by the guillotine procedure that nearly cost me my life some years earlier. He was a most beautiful operator who taught me the use of scissor dissections in a

46

confined space. It was a lesson that was to contribute enormously to my success in the operative treatment of cancer of the oesophagus.

My relationship with his senior colleague in Ear, Nose and Throat surgery however was not so happy. This particular consultant resented my appointment as I was preferred to a candidate who was one of his own students from St. Mary's Hospital. After a time he seemed to change his attitude and ultimately asked me out to dinner. There was very little off duty for house surgeons in London and I was officially "on duty" at the time but arranged for one of my colleagues to look after my patients while I accepted his invitation.

To my amazement and consternation I was reported the next morning to the hospital secretary for being out when I was on duty. Deeply upset by this incident, I felt convinced that he would oppose my re-appointment as at this particular time my job was due for renewal. Reluctantly, I decided to play him at his own game and decided on a strategy. I asked him for a testimonial as though I was going to resign. He seemed delighted and, in the belief that I was leaving, gave me a good testimonial to get rid of me. On the contrary, I did not resign but reapplied for the appointment using his own testimonial and was re-elected.

Duties in the Casualty Department were similar to those in the Accident and Emergency Departments of today but there were no Intensive Care Units. In cases of serious accident the ambulance would ring its bell as it entered the Casualty Department. On hearing the bell the doctor nearest to the Casualty Department ran to render assistance to the seriously ill. If, in fact, the patient was dead on arrival (BID - brought in dead) then the Coroner had to be informed and the informing doctor was given a fee of £3. As I was a good runner I was able to arrive at the Department before my slower colleagues and these Coroner's fees supplemented my salary of £125 per year and provided me with enough money for occasional visits to London's West End.

On one occasion an accident occurred at the Ealing Film Studios which were run at that time, I believe, by Gracie Fields the famous comedienne. A well know comedian colleague of hers called Harry Tate was injured in this accident. I looked after him and he later invited me to the studios and I found the visit most interesting. Subsequently he sent me a dedicated little poem, entitled, "How Could You Be So Kind".

The work of a junior hospital doctor was even more arduous than today, but life in London was interesting and exciting. The city was clean and the people polite and there was much to see and much to do. I felt a sense of freedom of thought and opinion that I have never experienced while living in Belfast. As time went on I came to realize that while in Ulster, my thoughts and actions were dictated by pre-conceptions and by prejudice both in politics and in religion. In the medical profession, however, I am glad to say that tolerance usually prevailed.

Having once being appointed to a London Hospital other opportunities presented themselves to extend experience in other hospitals in and around London. I spent a year working as Resident Medical Officer in the West Herts Hospital where though there were local general practitioners on the staff, the consultant staff were from the London Teaching Hospitals. At this hospital I had the pleasure of assisting Sir Gordon Gordon-Taylor* and greatly admired his technique in abdominal surgery and his kindly attitude to the patients and the staff.

During this period I became convinced that a career in surgery was what I really wanted and to this end was most fortunate to obtain the appointment of Resident Surgical Officer at Croydon General Hospital. This was at a time when I had not yet attained a Fellowship of the Royal College of Surgeons and was surprised that I had been given the job.

On the way to the interview for this appointment I called at a café near East Croydon station to have a cup of tea. I found the café entirely deserted and realized that this was at a time when Croydon was struck by a serious typhoid epidemic so that no one would eat or drink out in case they contracted the disease.

This epidemic was to prove of interest and embarrassment and ultimately the subject of a public enquiry.† The cases of typhoid occurred mainly in the Addiscombe Road which was a more opulent area where the inhabitants were in the older age groups, and in consequence were more adversely affected by the disease. One of the general practitioners, a Dr Dorothy Day showed a special interest in this epidemic and charted the occurrence of cases on a map. She came to the conclusion from the

---

* Sir Gordon Gordon-Taylor, Senior Surgeon, The Middlesex Hospital, London.

† Ministry of Health. Report into an outbreak of Typhoid Fever 1937. H.M. Stationery Office.

distribution of the cases that the infection was water-borne, and that the Addington water supply system was involved.

At this very time I received a letter from South Africa stating that in years gone by there had been a problem with the "Well at Addington" and the writer wondered if this might have been the cause of the present problem. The possibility that the epidemic could be water-borne was not regarded highly by the Medical Officer of Health who stated that there was no necessity to boil drinking water and that in any case the water was chlorinated. He felt that the infection might have come from water-cress, but this was vigorously denied by the Watercress Growers Association which said that their members maintained the highest standards of public health measures. A suggestion that the epidemic was milk-borne was equally vigorously denied.

In the event it was indeed discovered that the infection was in fact water-borne and that the Addington Well was at fault. Quite astonishingly a known typhoid carrier was at work repairing the Addington Well.

In addition to this, a misunderstanding arose between the Medical Officer of Health and the Borough Engineer. There was a period of time when the Borough Engineer thought the Medical Officer was chlorinating the water while the Medical Officer thought that the Borough Engineer was chlorinating the water; in the event the water was not chlorinated at all during a critical period. During this period of non-chlorination a secondary epidemic of typhoid occurred.

The details of this report are put in to emphasize the reason why, when I went into a café in George Street in Croydon, there was no one in the café; everyone feared eating out in Croydon and restaurants were deserted.[6]

In due course I arrived at the hospital for interview. I remember that there were two surgeons on the committee that appointed me to the post of Resident Surgical Officer. The first was the chairman Colonel Cowell who was the senior surgeon at the hospital. He subsequently had a very distinguished career in Army surgery, first of all in the Spanish Civil War in which he studied blood transfusion problems and then in the Second World War during which he became a Major-General.

As a matter of fact I was subsequently to meet his son Robert just before the war, and he was to become a very famous case of sex change.

When I met him he was, I believe, a pilot in the RAF. Years later after I had returned from the Middle East I met him again, but by this time he had undergone a sex change and was now known as Roberta.

The other surgeon was a Mr Clement Treves Neve, a local surgeon, who was a nephew of the famous Sir Frederick Treves, a surgeon to His Majesty The King. He was reputed to be an expert in the treatment of peritonitis, a feature that has been recorded in a mnemonic for medical students trying to remember the relationships of the structures in the knee joint. The mnemonic read "Treves is an Excellent Surgeon Especially in Peritonitis", the capital letters being the first letters of the structures on the surface of the knee joint.

Duties as Resident Surgical Officer started on 1 January 1938 at a time when Britain was a peace. All pre-occupations were directed to obtaining experience and training in surgery in what was the most senior and responsible post in surgery that I had ever held. The work was extremely hard but was exciting and stimulating. I was gaining experience in operating and realized that surgery was for me to be all absorbing.

So obsessed with my work, I was at first oblivious of the serious political developments in Germany and Hitler's rise to power. However, in time these problems began to intrude and when Neville Chamberlain, our Prime Minister returned from his meeting with Hitler in Munich waving a piece of paper declaring friendship and peace between Germany and Britain, I wondered what the future would hold. The Munich Agreement proved valueless and for me an appointment at Croydon which began in peace was to end in the midst of turmoil and of war.

7

The Eve of the Storm

THE importance of events are seldom realized at the time of their occurrence but rather in retrospect. While at Croydon General Hospital there were professional, personal and national occurrences which were to affect the entire future.

The Consultant Staff were drawn from London Teaching Hospitals and were of great distinction. Mr Alan Todd from Guy's Hospital was an orthopaedic surgeon of great academic distinction, whose son, following his father's footsteps became a distinguished general surgeon and was elected President of the Royal College of Surgeons of England.* Mr Douglas McLaggan from the Royal Free Hospital was the Consultant Ear Nose and Throat Surgeon and became Surgeon to H.M. Household† was a great help to me in a time of family illness when my brother Maurice, who had entered general practice, developed a mastoid infection. The third surgeon was perhaps the most unusual and interesting personality of the three. He was an Australian called E. C. T. Milligan‡ who came to England as a surgeon, with the rank of major in the Australian Expeditionary Force in the First World War.

Milligan was sent to the Western Front and was appalled by the incidence of infection and gangrene in war wounds. He decided that all the damaged tissue round the injury should be cut out entirely leaving the remaining tissues fresh and healthy. The procedure was called primary wound excision. This technique caused a furore with the surgeons

---

* Sir Ian Todd. Past President Royal College of Surgeons England
† Sir Douglas McLaggan. Surgeon to H.M. Royal Household.
‡ E. C. T. Milligan O.B.E., Surgeon to St. Marks Hospital, London.

51

of the day who felt that the procedure was removing a tissue defence area known then as the "pyogenic membrane". The procedure was roundly condemned and Milligan lost his rank of major and was reduced to a general duty officer.

Two years later when an American surgeon (Winnett Orr) described primary wound excision as a new and revolutionary treatment, Milligan's work was at last recognized and he had his rank of major restored and was awarded the Order of the British Empire. It is indeed on Milligan's principle of primary wound excision that the entire edifice of wound management is based today.

Milligan became a consultant at St. Mark's Hospital, which was and is world famous in the treatment of rectal diseases. Patiently and step by step he taught me rectal and colonic surgery and I learned from him to recognize tissue planes and the importance of clean cutting and of atraumatic surgery. I assisted him as he developed an operation for piles known to this day as Milligan's Haemorrhoidectomy.

At that time he was also developing a technique for removing cancer of the rectum, in which two surgeons were operating at the same time. The idea was quite revolutionary as in former years only one surgeon performed this operation. The technique became known as synchronous combined abdomino-perineal excision of the rectum (A.P.E.R.), and one surgeon worked upwards from the back passage, while the other worked downwards from the abdomen and, as it were, they joined up in the middle. The procedure has become a landmark of progress in the treatment of cancer of the lower bowel.

Milligan became a life long friend and in later years when I was on military service in the Middle East he never failed to call at my home and see that my family were well.

It was while working as a resident surgical officer at Croydon General Hospital that I met and fell in love with Joan Waugh. She was an extremely pretty lady, the daughter of a commander in the Royal Navy who had been decorated in the First World War and soon was to be re-decorated in the Second.

Commander Waugh was a fellow officer, on board H.M.S. *Renown*, of Edward, Prince of Wales during the visit to India and the Far East in

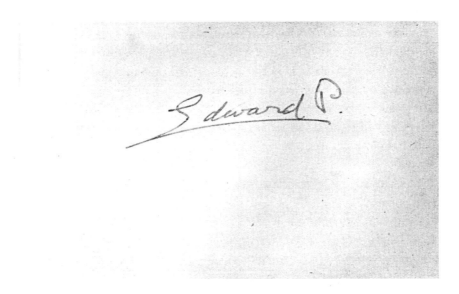

FIGURE 2. *Original Composition of* God Bless the Prince of Wales *by Samuel Fairfield on 23 May 1922, and the signature of the Prince.*

1921/22. It was during this visit that Samuel Fairfield, Director of Music to His Royal Highness, composed the anthem *God Bless the Prince of Wales*. (Fig. 2). This was written on Tuesday, 23 May 1922 while the ship was off Penang. Prince Edward was later to become King Edward VIII and was to abdicate and marry an American lady, Mrs. Simpson.

The work load in the hospital was heavy. In such spare time as was available at the week-ends, Joan and I played tennis at the hospital where one was immediately available for any emergency. There was seldom a set that was not interrupted by the hospital porter or the casualty nurse appearing at the tennis court with a pre-arranged system of signs indicating the urgency of the call.

Dancing was the other recreation that both of us liked. Whenever possible Joan and I would go to a road house near Hildenborough in Kent which was run by a retired colonel of the Indian Army and which was called The Old Barn. The menu was simple and the licence was limited but dinner jackets had to be worn.

On one very special occasion on 3 May 1938 we went to the Dorcester for the annual dinner of the Queen's University Club which was very much a white tie affair. Joan borrowed her sister's fur stole for this special occasion. As we danced the foxtrot and waltzes of this time the fur stole moulted and my newly acquired tail jacket was covered with rabbit hair.

Personal affairs were soon to be submerged in the international catastrophe which was about to happen. Early in 1938, my chief, E. T. C. Milligan, was on a visit to Germany to describe the special operation which he had worked out for the treatment of piles. On his return I met him at Croydon aerodrome which was the London airport of pre-war years.

As we drove from the airport to the hospital in his old open-top touring Rolls Royce he told me that Hitler was re-arming, and he felt sure that Germany was preparing for war. Soon there was to be the putsch in Austria and the German walk into Czechoslovakia and with this the slippery slope to war had commenced. Even Neville Chamberlain's paper agreement, waved aloft on the steps of the aircraft after the Munich visit, failed to reassure the British people and defence preparations began to be made with great urgency. It was a difficult time professionally as the future seemed dark indeed though one could not but appreciate that a surgeon is of as great a value in war as in peace.

8

Surgeon in the London Blitz

THINKING of the German influence in the Spanish Civil War it seemed that London would be a primary target at the outbreak of war. Colonel Cowell, the senior local surgeon at Croydon General Hospital had spent some time in the civil war in Spain and became an important source of information to the Government on air raid precautions.

The London area was divided into nine sectors with a Teaching Hospital at the apex in central London and the base hospitals on the periphery in the home counties. I joined the Emergency Medical Services as a surgeon and was in Sector 9. The Teaching Hospital was King's College Hospital and the base hospitals were at Epsom and Leatherhead. The younger surgeons were stationed in London and the more senior and experienced consultants were in relative safety in the base hospitals. It was realized that in the First World War the senior surgeons were soon killed off in the battle front and it was rightly agreed that their skills and safety must be preserved and that the same mistake was not be made again in the Second World War as was made in the First.

I was at Croydon when the first air raid alert sounded. It happened just as Mr Chamberlain, the Prime Minister, was announcing that we were in a state of war with Germany. The effect was electric and we all rushed into the shelters thinking that the whole city was in immediate danger of annihilation and wondering if we did survive what would it all be like. But nothing happened and it was all a mistake. An unidentified aircraft that had crossed the coast was thought to be German and so the alert was sounded; it proved to be a false alarm.

There followed a period of quiet which became known as "the phoney war". While Hitler was engaged in the invasion of Poland and in tight-

55

ening his grip on the middle European states all was quiet on the Western Front. Bored with the inactivity I studied hard and attained the Fellowship of the Royal College of Surgeons of Edinburgh and the Mastership of Surgery at the Queen's University in Belfast. It was at this time I embarked on my first research project.

In Sector 9 was Queen Mary's Hospital, Carshalton, which was perhaps the biggest Children's Hospital in England. Its 1400 beds were in pavilions arranged in branches round a central core—rather like a pine tree in structure. I spent the first year of the war in this hospital and at the Mayday Hospital in Croydon.

At Queen Mary's Hospital I was impressed with the problems produced by two main disease, the first was poliomyelitis (infantile paralysis) and the other was osteomyelitis (infection of bone). There were several hundred cases of children under the age of fifteen who were paralysed in various degrees by infantile paralysis while there were some 800 cases suffering from osteomyelitis.

Osteomyelitis was an acute infective and septicaemic disease which carried a high death rate at its onset. If the patient survived the acute disease they could spend years in and out of hospitals with recurrent bone abscesses and with infective discharging wounds. They would be submitted to dozens of operations to remove dead pieces of bone as they occurred from time to time. I reviewed these cases and found that if osteomyelitis affected the femur (thigh bone), the patients could spend up to five years of their young lives in hospital, while if the pelvic bones were affected their time in hospital would be even longer.

At this time the treatment of the disease was solely surgical. The affected bone was opened up by chiselling away the outer layers of the bone to drain the underlying bone abscess. This extensive process caused further bone to die and led to the necessity of repeated operations and very long periods in hospital.

In 1936 the discovery of sulphonamides (the M & B group of drugs) was the first step in the effective treatment of infection. I felt that if this drug were to be used in osteomyelitis, extensive operations on the bone might be avoided and that just drilling holes in the bone rather than opening up of the bone might be sufficient. The first case was a boy of fifteen with osteomyelitis of the thigh bone who was treated by this new method. The treatment worked splendidly and he was cured in a period of only five weeks.

At this time the Consultant Orthopaedic Surgeon at Queen Mary's Hospital was a Mr Lambrinudi, the Senior Surgeon at Guy's Hospital. He was an outstanding and original thinker and had spent much of his time at Carshalton carrying out the transplant of tendons to diminish the disabilities arising from infantile paralysis. I showed him this case and he was so interested that he arranged for all acute osteomyelitic cases south of the river Thames to be sent to Queen Mary's Hospital for this new treatment. With such a wide population in London to draw upon a considerable number of cases were treated in a very short time and confirmed the success of this concept. To my astonishment he asked me to present these cases at the Royal Society of Medicine[7] when he was President of the section of Orthopaedics. Ultimately twenty-eight cases were treated and the stay in hospital was measured in weeks and not in years.[8] This was to herald a new era in the treatment of infections.

The use of sulphonamides in the treatment of war wounds was subsequently tried out in the Middle East by Sir Heneage Ogilvie and with considerable success; an experience later confirmed by those of us who were to treat war wounds in London.

Two years later Fleming and Florey addressed a highly selective audience at the Royal Society of Medicine in London to introduce penicillin which was the breakthrough of the century.

I was delighted when Florey quoted my paper on the use of sulphonamides in acute osteomyelitis. In the years that followed the validity of this work was fully substantiated.

Then suddenly the phoney war was over and the war commenced in earnest. Hitler's *Luftwaffe* began to attack our airfields. I watched the German Stuka airplanes dive with their bombs on Croydon aerodrome which with Kenley and Biggin Hill formed the main part of the R.A.F. defence of London. It is interesting to note that there were, I believe, as many casualties in this first five minute raid on Croydon aerodrome as there were in the whole of the Falkland War.

And so began the Battle of Britain as the Few engaged the *Luftwaffe* in aerial dog fights over London and the fields of Kent and Surrey. In the blue skies of this lovely summer of 1940 the vapour trails of aircraft weaving about were punctuated with white puffs of smoke from exploding anti-aircraft shells. The roar of aircraft plunging to their doom and the quiet opening of a parachute were all part of this fantastic scene.

It was at this time that Joan and I were married at All Saints Church in Sanderstead, a ceremony interrupted by the screech of bombs and all the noise of aerial bombardment. A week-end honeymoon, followed by the evacuation of our new home because of a time bomb near our garden was to set the scene for the next few years.

My best man was an old friend from Queen's called W. H. H. (Harry) McIlroy. He was a remarkable person who seemed to live a charmed life and is still alive today. After some incredible escapes in the London blitz he joined the Royal Navy as a surgeon lieutenant. He was posted to one of the latest designed destroyers, H.M.S. *Marne*. Following commissioning tests in the North Sea the ship escorted convoys to Russia. After narrowly missing being ice-bound in Barrents Sea his ship was torpedoed off Gibraltar. He had just left the sick quarters of the ship to help with some survivors who were being rescued from the sea when his own ship was torpedoed. The section where he had just been was completely destroyed and though becalmed and immobilized in a quiet sea the attacking submarine did not make a further attack, presumably it had run out of torpedoes.

The day time air raids during the week seemed to be timed to occur in the morning or in the evening when people were going to or returning from work but at the week-end the heavy raids seemed to occur at lunchtime.

On one occasion Joan and I were sheltering under the stairs of our home in South Croydon when a man in uniform came through the french doors which had been blown open by the raid. He was ashen grey and when I spoke to him he did not reply. Joan was sure that he was a German parachutist and we locked the unprotesting man in the kitchen. We found later, however, that he was an air raid warden who, though he had no outward sign of physical damage, was concussed by an exploding bomb which had killed his colleague who was standing beside him at his air raid shelter.

The casualties in London were heavy and I was posted back to King's

College Hospital. There were two young surgeons, John Peel* and A. J. Heriot who worked at the hospital.† The three of us worked happily together forming a major surgical unit in South London. When the Battle of Britain was won by the courage and skill of the "Few" R.A.F. pilots, the day attacks were replaced by raids at night which were less intense but more prolonged. The occurrence of air raid casualties did not lessen the need for the treatment of the ordinary sick population. As time went on a routine evolved in which during the day one treated ordinary civilian patients and at night the air raid casualties.

Each day we evacuated all those who were fit enough to travel to the base hospitals at Epsom and at Leatherhead and sometimes to St. Lawrence's Hospital at Caterham. I was allocated, in the absence on active service of two of the consultant staff, two surgical clinics, that of Harold Edwards whose specialty was gastro-enterology and that of Edward Muir who was a general surgeon with special interest in colonic and rectal diseases. It was this experience and the interest gained in these clinics that formed my future surgical career.

The pressure of work, both day and night, was unbelievable and provided experience to surgeons of my generation never to be repeated. Bad weather was welcome because it caused a lull in the air raids and allowed us to catch up with sleep. Every three months, house surgeons would leave to enter the service and we had a party with the meagre supplies of drink that were available.

As time went on fatigue and poor diet reduced the vitality of us all. It was important to acquire the habit of sleep even for a few minutes if the time were available. In a heavy night attack we would drag our mattresses into the main corridor for increased safety and the entire staff would sleep on the floor.

On one occasion I was wakened from a deep sleep by the night porter who was seeking Mr Peel. I pointed down the corridor to where I thought he was and promptly fell asleep again. In what seemed hours later the porter awakened me again to tell me that he had found him and I felt

---

* Later Sir John Peel, K.C.V.O., F.R.C.S., Surgeon Gynaecologist to H.M. The Queen. Consultant in Obstetrics, King's College Hospital
† A. J. Heriot, M.S., F.R.C.S. Consultant Surgeon, King's College Hospital

that I would like to have committed a murder; it was a time when labour was short and even those mentally retarded were employed.

On another occasion I was called at night by the Anglo-American ambulance to go to St. Lawrence's Hospital in Caterham to see a very special casualty. I felt it must be Churchill himself, so great was the urgency. But things turned out to be very different. The patient himself was a mental defective who had an obsession to have everything flat. He was employed as a bulldozer driver on Kenley R.A.F. Station and his job was to fill in the bomb craters on the runway caused by German dive bombers. Because of his obsession he could not tolerate the presence of craters and would fill them in even in positions of great danger when a raid was actually in progress. That was obviously why he was injured and also why it was so important to save his life and to get him back on duty.

In time of war it is natural that surgery should take precedence over medicine, but this in no way diminished the problems facing physicians, for a patient may die of diabetes as easily as from a war injury. In King's College Hospital the General Medical Unit was under the charge of Dr J. Gilpin and Dr Bruce Pearson. The Diabetic Unit was one of very special importance. It was under the charge of Dr R. D. Lawrence with Dr Oakley as second in command.

Dr Lawrence was quite a remarkable man whose name had become a household word in the field of diabetes. As a young man he had the great ambition to be a surgeon but while operating on a patient with an abscess, some infection entered his eye and the eye had to be removed. It was discovered that he was a diabetic. As insulin had not yet been discovered, the outlook for a young diabetic was hopeless and an early death was inevitable. A lover of the city of Florence, he left England to live in Italy, for his survival was thought to be short indeed.

At this time, however, Banting and Best (1926) discovered insulin and by good fortune supplies of this new substance had been allocated to King's College Hospital. On hearing this, he had his chauffeur drive him from Florence to London where he was admitted to the hospital.

The dose of insulin to be administered to him was not at this stage precisely known and, after his first injection, he collapsed into hypoglycaemic coma from too much insulin. On recovering, he decided to study diabetes extensively and to establish a unit at King's College Hospital where he soon attained international reputation.

Lawrence's interest in surgery was by no means finished. There is a condition of sepsis and gangrene occurring in the feet of patients with diabetes, known as diabetic foot. In 1941 treatment was above-knee amputation and foot conservation was unknown. Lawrence sent for me to go to his clinic and I went with great curiosity as to why such a senior consultant wanted to speak to a very junior surgeon. He showed me a case of diabetic foot and I suggested that the only treatment was an above-knee amputation. He asked me however, if I would remove only part of the foot by cutting a wedge out of the foot as one would cut a wedge out of a cake or cut a section out of a rotten apple. I was astonished at this suggestion which was contrary to all I had been taught, but reluctantly agreed to carry out his precise instruction.

The procedure was a great success and the patient's foot was preserved. This was followed by the treatment of many other cases along this revolutionary line.[9] The clinical concepts of Lawrence have recently been fully explained by the researches of Dr Andrew Boulton, the Senior Lecturer in Medicine at the Royal Infirmary in Manchester. Dr Boulton has offered an explanation of the occurrence of the diabetic foot which he presented recently in the thirteenth Lawrence Memorial Lecture given at the annual meeting of the British Diabetic Association.[10]

Lawrence and I became good friends and in the intervals between air raids we played tennis on the courts at King's College Hospital. He always won the first set 6–0 but in the second set he became slightly hypoglycaemic (short of glucose in the blood) and hit wildly at the ball. I was able to win the second set but in war time we had not the energy for a third set.

As the months passed by, air raid casualties were absorbed in the ordinary days work. Alarmed by the effect of bombing on the Londoner, Churchill switched all the anti-aircraft defences to London so that when the German airplanes arrived they were greeted with an immense amount of fire. Most of this was inaccurate and few planes were shot down. It was at this time however, that the *Luftwaffe* switched their attack from London to the provincial towns. Some of these attacks on the provincial cities were of great severity and the attack on Coventry was intense and devastating.

It was a depressing feature that such attacks could take place with few enemy aircraft being destroyed and many of the casualties probably resulted from our own anti-aircraft fire. But things were about to change though the change was gradual. It became obvious that the searchlights which had probed the sky unsuccessfully for so long, now began to fix on the German bombers, and the anti-aircraft fire became more effective.

I remember one lovely but dreaded moonlit night, I think it was 6 May 1941, when the alert sounded and the sky seemed full of German bombers. To my surprise there was virtually no anti-aircraft fire and I became very puzzled and wondered if we had run out of ammunition. However, instead of the usual thunderous gun fire one could hear in the sky machine gun and cannon fire and German aircraft began to be destroyed.

This success was at the time attributed to the skills of the R.A.F. night fighters, and one very famous pilot called Cunningham was thought to possess superb night vision. He was therefore nicknamed "Cats-eyes" or "Carrots" Cunningham as carrots were said to improve night vision, and his mother said on the radio that her son always liked carrots.

There was no doubt, however, that he was a superb pilot but all these successes were not due to good night vision but were due to the fact that we had by then invented radar. This helped not only the searchlights and the guns to locate their targets but also the night fighters could then see their targets on the radar screen.

From this time on the threat of both night and daytime bombing receded and surgical work in London resumed a more civilian aspect. With better protection from air attack our factories could work more consistently and in greater safety and our war effort became greatly enhanced.

9

The Second Front

WITH the Allied successes in the Middle East, and the great struggle by the Russians on the Eastern Front, there was great pressure to open a battle front in Western Europe. At the same time there were rumours of German secret weapons of destruction and the medical services were wondering what new problems the future held in store. Military convoys were everywhere and our own medical arrangements were altered in preparation for the Second Front.

Each surgeon had a team that was mobile. It consisted of a surgeon in charge, an assistant, an anaesthetist, a theatre sister and a medical student whose duty was really that of a medical secretary but was known as a "scribe". This team system had many advantages which became even more apparent as experience with the system began to grow. The presence of a theatre sister as a constant member of the team was of greatest importance and led to an operative efficiency that is seldom equalled today.

The present trend of constant changes in the theatre staff under the guise of training is indeed a most retrograde step and produces a poor standard of theatre work. The other feature was the inclusion of a "scribe" in the operative team. This member of the team was really a medical secretary who helped with all the records and clinical notes thereby enabling the surgeon to concentrate on the many clinical problems that were to be encountered in these immensely busy days.

In later years I regarded this idea so highly that I introduced it into my clinics in Darlington Memorial Hospital, where I had a full time secretary looking after all the needs of the clinic and of the wards. This enormously increased the throughput of patients in the clinic and immensely increased the efficiency of the surgical unit. Clinical notes were therefore readable and full and this provided a basis for clinical research purposes.

It was this experience which convinced me that, to increase the throughput of a unit, staff must be deployed around the clinician to facilitate his work, and not round an administrative structure, which only creates paperwork and contributes nothing to the quality or the quantity of clinical care.

As preparations for the Second Front became more advanced each mobile surgical unit was allocated a hospital. I was moved from King's College Hospital to the base hospital at Leatherhead. Just before D-Day I went with my team to the allotted hospital at Leatherhead and Joan went to live in a rented house in South Croydon.

Soon after D-Day the first convoys of casualties from the beaches arrived at the hospital. They were quite an extraordinary group both in type of injury and in their nationality. Strangely enough amongst the first convoys there were many nationalities without any Germans amongst them. It was apparent that the German coastal defences were a mixture of unwilling and conscripted soldiers from areas under German domination. The first German soldiers I encountered were terrified as I approached them to determine their injuries. I had a feeling that they had been told that they would be liquidated as were so many Jews and other nationals in Germany itself. After operation they appeared to be immensely relieved and much more cheerful.

As the convoys came rolling in we operated on a team system of eight hours on and eight hours off. This means that in one day we would operate for sixteen hours and the following day for only eight.

I had the privilege of staying at the home of Mr J. G. Yates-Bell, who was the senior urologist at King's College Hospital and who had a delightful home in Leatherhead.

On one special occasion in June 1944 after a long day's operating I noted as I went to bed that I heard a new type of aircraft noise with which I was unfamiliar. At this time we were all familiar with the sounds of Hurricanes, Spitfires and the various types of German plane. But this new noise was different and strangely the engine suddenly cut out and there were some great explosions from the London area that could be heard clearly in Leatherhead. Next morning I was called by Yates-Bell

FIGURE 3. *Hitler's secret weapon—the V1 Flying Bomb which became known as the* Doodlebug, *and caused great devastation.*

at 6.00 a.m. saying that my wife Joan had been bombed out. I got up instantly and made my way to Croydon where I was able to learn the cause of the strange aircraft noise that I had heard the previous day. It was the attack on London by flying bombs—the V1 secret weapon soon to be known as "doodlebugs" (Fig. 3)—which were to kill 8,000 people. As I passed along I saw many of these strange aircraft flying overhead on their deadly course. Our temporary home was in Selson Road just opposite a large wooded area known Croham Hurst.

As I travelled up the hill from South Croydon I came on a scene which was quite terrible. A flying bomb had landed in the trees at Croham Hurst and the entire row of houses opposite the Hurst was destroyed. There was no bomb crater, but every roof and every wall was flattened by the surface blast. Bricks, glass, debris and items of furniture were scattered everywhere and even on the top of a defoliated tree there was a child's teddy bear fantastically entangled in its branches.

It was not only the sight but also the feeling of destruction and desolation that was so disturbing and to realize that we were left with nothing except the clothes that we were wearing.

By the greatest good fortune Joan and all the residents had been in a large surface shelter which was split across its centre, but the only casualty was an old woman who had bumped her head against a wooden bench. All the occupants were very shaken indeed but Joan had survived with nothing worse than shock. Then the problem suddenly dawned on me as to where we could go, as all the houses had gone. With no possessions whatever, we got into the car to go back to Leatherhead where my next operating shift was about due to start.

Joan was accommodated in a room below the operating theatre for three days until we could move to a room in the living quarters of a little inn called the Running Horses near Mickleham. We lived there for a few more days, but then a stray flying bomb, miles off course, landed in the village and I felt that it was then time for her to be evacuated. This particular flying bomb had a curious effect in that, in our room, all the glass and curtains were sucked out and not blown in as one would have expected. The furniture careered around the room and a chest of drawers hurled across the room was suddenly sucked back ending up in its original position, with all the drawers neatly closed as though it had never moved. I never quite knew how this could take place.

With my wife and her own family safely evacuated to Ross-on-Wye the work on the Second Front victims continued but with a diminishing work load as the Army Medical Service began to establish its own hospitals across the Channel. On the other hand the civilian casualties in London were increasing because of the flying bombs and also from another of Hitler's secret weapons the V2 rockets.

I was posted back to King's College Hospital to rejoin my former colleagues and settled down again to both civilian and air raid casualties. I had an interesting experience of seeing a V2 rocket land in Camberwell Green and after it exploded one could hear the sound of its coming long after it had arrived , indicating that it was travelling considerably faster than the speed of sound. It was interesting to contemplate that some German airman or soldier on the other side of the English Channel was manipulating controls which directed the missile to land in London. At that time one could foresee further developments in radio controlled bombs which were to culminate in the Cruise Missile, but the degree of accuracy of control as demonstrated recently in the Gulf War is a fantastic scientific achievement.

In due course, after some months, the bombing situation settled down and the family returned to South Croydon where we bought a house and at this stage we were expecting our family. At this time, also, Brigadier Harold Edwards and Colonel Edward Muir who were on active service overseas returned home, enabling me to enter the service. I was gazetted as a surgical specialist in the Royal Army Medical Corps and entered a new and different milieu.

10

Surgeon in Khaki

THE Royal Army Medical Corps Training Depot is in Crookham near Aldershot, and it was to this unit that I was sent for military training. After years of overwork and on a meagre war time civilian diet in London the physical strain was at first very considerable. It was remarkable, however, that on generous army rations and graduated drill how full physical vigour could soon be restored. The meat eaten for one single meal in the army was the equivalent of a month's ration as a civilian. The drills and physical training were interspersed with lectures on army structure and procedure and this opened up a new field of experience.

After completion of training it was usual to have a posting in the United Kingdom before going overseas. As our twin boys had recently been born and were living in Croydon, I asked for a posting to Southern Command.

I was promptly posted to York Military Hospital in Northern Command. The work in this hospital was very much lighter than that to which I had become accustomed and I spent some time visiting the local civilian hospital. It was at York County Hospital that I met a very brilliant technical surgeon Mr Headley Visick.

We both shared a special interest in gastric surgery and in particular the removal of part of the stomach (partial gastrectomy) for the treatment of duodenal ulcer. His technique was excellent but he became almost intoxicated with the procedure itself and carried out a much too extensive removal of the stomach. This was the only point on which we disagreed. In subsequent years it became apparent that extensive gastrectomy lead to malnutrition whereas conservative resections were equally satisfactory in curing the ulcer and did not cause this complication.

It was also while at York that I first heard of the town of Northallerton, mainly because of the accidents from the large number of R.A.F. bomber stations which were scattered over the North Riding of Yorkshire. At this time I did not think even for one moment that it would be in this area that I would ultimately do my major surgical work.

The posting to York Military Hospital was a short one and I was soon on Draft for overseas service. The posting was to the Middle East and we travelled across the Mediterranean by troopship. The ship was an Italian freighter, the *Bamfora*. It was of about 7000 tons and we were accommodated in rows of army bunks in the cargo holds. The ship had a strange characteristic which may well have allowed its survival throughout the war. While on deck the ship did not seem to be going in the direction in which it was pointing and it was perhaps this crab like movement that confused the German U boat commanders so that the torpedoes failed to find the target!

The voyage through the Mediterranean was hot and uncomfortable but it provided a period of complete idleness that I had never experienced for many years. In the London blitz life was hectic and each day and most nights were spent operating or on other surgical duties. There was no time for thought or contemplation, and everything was done with a sense of urgency. But on the troopship things were different, and other than the routine boat drill there was little to do. On the foredeck the men seemed to play Housey Housey from morning to night and the calling out of the numbers became almost unbearable, so I sought refuge as far away from the foredeck as possible.

In this time of contemplation I looked back on my work as a hospital doctor and taking the first steps on the surgical ladder. As one grows in life, as in surgery, certain people influence development and the person one is to become. In surgery I learned the skilled use of a scissor dissection from C. P. Wilson, the Consultant Ear Nose and Throat surgeon at the Middlesex Hospital which helped me years later when I embarked on the surgical treatment of cancer of the gullet. The gentle handling of human tissue at operation was exemplified by the work of Sir Gordon Gordon-Taylor also of the Middlesex Hospital. The definition of tissue planes was epitomized in the work of Mr E. C. T. Milligan at St. Mark's Hospital, while precision of surgical technique was the hall-mark of Cecil Joll at the Royal Free Hospital.

In each of these aspects of surgery I modelled my development on the work of these great masters of surgery. At this time the success of surgery was dependent on operative technique alone, and surgeons strove to attain perfection in the operating theatre and this feature produced a generation of artistic masters of surgery.

In modern times the major advances in anaesthesia, the immediate availability of blood transfusion, the intricacies of modern technology, the use of the intensive care unit and antibiotics all combine to support the surgeon in a way that was undreamed of when I was a very young surgeon. Surgeons of lesser skills can now obtain results as good as those obtained by the great masters of surgery because of these recent advances.

The immense workload during the war in London provided an un-precedented and unrepeatable opportunity for practise and experience in surgery and in the development of operative technique. I realized that by chance and good fortune I, at a very young age, had been able to obtain these essential ingredients to attain excellence in surgery.

What was still very uncertain was the attainment of success in a career. The disruption of war had affected the profession and the political structure and the social order was likely to change, so the future was to be a period of profound uncertainty. I decided that there was nothing I could do about the position and resolved just to concentrate on the day to day duties as an army surgeon and to leave the future to take care of itself.

NORTH AFRICA

I shall never forget my first glimpse of the Middle East and of an Arab family. The father was travelling with his family and wearing his galabea and sitting not on the back of the donkey but over the donkeys hips. A heavy burden was straddled across the donkey's back, and the Arab kept goading the animal by digging his naked heels into the donkey's side, while his galabea kept flapping around the animal's hind legs. Walking in line behind were four women with their faces half covered by yashmaks as is the Arab custom. Each woman carried a vessel on her head with amazing skill and grace, while they led their children by each hand. I was soon to learn that Arab men were permitted to have four wives, who were little better than slaves. It seemed to me a man's world in which women walked, carried burdens, and led children while the husbands rode on the donkey.

Disembarkation was with military precision and we were taken by Army trucks to the R.A.M.C. base depot near Heliopolis. It was indeed a hot and barren camp on the outskirts of Cairo and on the edge of the desert. Each day our draft was reduced in numbers as postings of the various officers and men were made all over the Middle East from Asmara in Eritrea to Tripoli in North Africa. We all feared a posting to Shaiba, a miserable and extremely hot station on the Persian Gulf near to Basra. I was relieved when my posting came through as Surgical Specialist to the 82nd General Hospital in Benghazi. I knew where Benghazi was and that it was on the Mediterranean Sea and was the capital of Cyrenaica.

The journey was interesting. We started by train from Cairo and travelled along the costal edge of the Libyan Plateau through Mersa Matruh and Sidi Barrani to reach Tobruk where the railroad ends. Tobruk was a devastated town surrounded by a ridge of land on which was strewn all the debris of the various battles that had raged so recently. The minefields were still in place and the harbour was littered with sunken ships.

The onward journey from Tobruk was by 15 cwt. truck, travelling along the coastal road to Derna, an attractive Arab village, which had largely escaped the desert battles. This was because our attacking forces proceeded in a line straight across the centre of Cyrenaica to reach Benghazi leaving Derna by-passed and virtually untouched. It was at Derna that I first saw bougainvillaea, that beautiful tropical climbing plant with the purple tips to its green leaves.

Benghazi was a well-built but battle scarred town which had been built and brought into prominence by Mussolini. It was to this area that before the war unemployed Italian citizens were deported from their homelands, supplied with the means of existence and implanted in farms where they were told to make their living.

The outstanding features of Benghazi were the harbour and the cathedral. The harbour was splendid but the cathedral even more re-markable. The cathedral had two generously rounded and identical domes sited close together and which the troops had nicknamed Mae West for obvious reasons. The town was extremely severely damaged but from what remained one could visualize that in time of peace it was a very pleasant Italian colonial town.

THE 82ND GENERAL HOSPITAL

The 82nd General Hospital was accommodated in an Italian built hospital situated on the edge of the town. Over the front door was a symbol and the Roman figure 17, indicating that the building was constructed in the seventeenth year of Mussolini's government (Fig. 4). Next to the hospital was a native shanty town constructed of petrol tins and oil drums to accommodate the native survivors who were rendered homeless by the battles in Benghazi.

The hospital was a 250-bed Military Hospital equipped to deal with all the forces under British Command. Close at hand was another hospital under the civilian authority but manned by locally enlisted army staff which looked after the local native population. The surgeon at the 82nd General Hospital whom I was to replace was Major W. M. Dennison who had been promoted Lieutenant-Colonel and was ultimately to

FIGURE 4. *Officers of the 82nd General Hospital in Benghazi. The Roman symbol over the entrance indicates that the hospital was built in the seventeenth year of the Italian dictator Mussolini's rule.*
(Author front 3rd right. Centre: Lt. Col. John B. Neal, Commanding Officer.)

become a leading paediatric surgeon in Glasgow Royal Infirmary on his return to civilian life.

The work at the hospital was that of any Military Hospital but to this was added a very special interest. Not only did the hospital deal with the medical problems of British Troops, but also those of native troops including members of the West African Frontier Force, and in addition a large number of Italian prisoners of war. It was perhaps the West African troops who provided the greatest clinical interest.

Entering army service as a surgical specialist I was not given any training or instruction in tropical diseases. This was to prove a great disadvantage since the native troops provided a never-ending series of strange tropical conditions that I had never seen or even read about. I saw for the first time yaws, schistosomiasis, guinea worm and a large variety of tropical ulcers which are completely unknown in temperate climates.

Perhaps the most interesting disease was a condition of abscess which occurred in the muscles over the back and was known as tropical pyo-myositis. This occurred mainly in tribesmen in the West African Frontier Defence Force. The condition appeared to be most common in the Hausas who were a warlike tribe from the northern part of Nigeria. The strange features about this condition were the size of the abscesses which occurred in the muscles, and the fact that we were frequently unable to grow organisms from the pus obtained from these abscesses. One would have expected the pus to be teaming with organisms but this surprisingly was not so. This condition of pyo-myositis has been highlighted recently by Mr D. F. Paton* of London who informs me that in his recent investigations he has shown that the patients with pyo-myositis are HIV positive. This might explain the failure to find organisms in the pus from the abscesses in these cases where the defence mechanisms were so impaired that even a few undetected organisms could cause major in-flammatory change. Could it be that AIDS was therefore present in Africa 40 years ago and has only now spread into the western world?

It was the custom of these West African soldiers to play a game with shells which they used as dice and played the game for money. During

---

* D. F. Paton F.R.C.S., F.R.C.S.E, Consultant Orthopaedic Surgeon Whittington Hospital, London

one of these sessions a loser refused to pay his debts so the friend with whom he was playing went to the armoury at Tyrelli barracks, drew his rifle and, as he was a marksman, only one round of ammunition. He returned to the barrack room where he shot the defaulter. By some miracle the bullet passed just under the back of his skull and though it rendered him temporarily unconscious it did no serious or permanent damage.

As I had operated on him I had to appear at a later date at the court martial to give evidence. This was an amazing experience because many interpreters, each using a different dialect, translated the questions and answers from one dialect to another before the culprit in the dock could understand what question was being asked. Similarly, his answers had many translators and I wondered if each interpreter was adding a bit of his own. The accused soldier was duly convicted but the court martial took the view that the crime was understandable in the circumstances and not too serious, so he was given detention for eighteen months!

In the desert plains of Barce near Benghazi herds of wild dogs roamed the land and rabies is endemic in these animals. Every British soldier likes to have a dog and it was even rumoured that the famous General Rommel was said to have been the former owner of the black labrador dog which lived in our mess and was called Blackie. Unfortunately, the local dogs become infected from contact with these wild herds.

It so happened that a dog with which I had been in close contact contracted rabies and died. Obviously I was very worried and had the dead dog's brain removed and sent by aircraft to a special laboratory in Khartoum.

Unfortunately, the light plane on its way to Cairo, the first stage of its journey, ran out of fuel and landed on the desert road. By the time relief fuel was provided there was such a delay that the heat had softened the brain and when it at last arrived at the laboratory in Khartoum, the tissue had degenerated and it was useless for diagnostic examination. Consequently, there was no absolute certainty that the dog had actually died of rabies. This part of the problem was solved by the fact that one other dog died of typical rabies so that the diagnosis was thought to be correct.

Because of this I started on a course of immunization which consisted of sixteen abdominal injections. These were most toxic and had a side effect of which I was not aware. I found that at the site of injections there was marked muscle weakness so that the strength of the abdominal muscles got less as the course of injections continued.

This was a side effect that had an amusing sequel. One evening after a heavy day when the General Officer Commanding had paid a visit, we were relaxing in the mess after the General had gone, when our hospital Commanding Officer seemed to get very fed up with the G.O.C.'s visit and had many more drinks than normal. I was unable to join in the celebrations as I had been forbidden to drink in view of the anti-rabies injections. In due course I helped the drunken Commanding Officer to his room which was next to my own and was connected by a balcony overlooking the front of the hospital.

I was wakened in the middle of the night by a strange noise and the sound of running water. I woke up and switched on the light and was astonished to see the Commanding Officer standing in the room looking rather dazed and fulfilling a function that made it obvious what was the cause of the sound of running water. He had mistaken my room for the bathroom and my round bedside chair for the toilet, an understandable mistake for a man who had rather drunk too much. I tried to escort him back to his room but seeing my empty bed he staggered to it and slumped into the bed and went fast asleep.

This situation was quite ridiculous because I was completely sober and he completely tight, and while I was up and awake he was lying asleep comfortably in my bed. He was a small man, and remembering my army training, I decided to give him a fireman's lift and cart him back to his own bed. I pulled his arm over my shoulder in the approved fashion but though my shoulders felt strong I could not lift him because with the injections the power of my abdominal muscles had gone. Frustrated, I left him in my bed and went off to his bed and fell fast asleep.

We shared a batman and the next morning as the batman brought in the usual cup of tea he looked strangely puzzled. He wondered if he could believe his eyes when he saw this switch over. I noted that the batman's consumption of beer fell remarkably in the weeks that followed this incident.

On the more serious side I hoped that the immunization against rabies would be successful. I realized that protection was no where near 100% but hoped for the best.

Rabies is perhaps one of the most terrible diseases known to man and is universally fatal so that the course of injections seemed to be essential. The immunization programme however is not without its danger and sometimes causes encephalitis and was said to have a risk of about ten per cent. This complication of encephalitis usually occurs during the latter part of the course of injections so each day was approached with apprehension and every headache considered serious.

To crown it all the incubation of rabies is from six weeks to two years, so there was a prolonged period of uncertainty in case the dreaded hydrophobia would herald a fatal outcome.

During my work at the 82nd General Hospital I was frequently called to the civil hospital to see cases in consultation. I was rather surprised from time to time by the nature of these consultations requested by the locally enlisted Captain in the R.A.M.C.

I was to learn some months later, when I was posted to Greece, that when he had left the hospital he had taken the surgical instruments with him. He was arrested while he journeyed through Tobruk on his way to Cairo, and was duly court martialled. At the court martial it was found that he was in fact only a medical student and had never actually qualified in medicine, but was locally enlisted in the Middle East into the army. He was of Greek extraction but unfortunately now I cannot even remember his name.

Work in a military hospital overseas was very different from that in a civilian hospital in the United Kingdom. In a very hot climate there are dangers of heat exhaustion to both patients and to staff. In consequence of this, operation lists were started at 7 a.m. or before and stopped at noon to avoid the hottest part of the day. The afternoon was a rest period and work started again at 5 p.m.

Though the majority of the patients were of British origin a substantial minority were from the African continent and some from the Far East. It came as a surprise that many of these Africans believed in witchcraft and voodoo and this produced situations which were a new experience to most surgeons of the west. Some native patients after a small operation like a repair of a hernia would "turn their faces to the wall" and die for no apparent reason.

The work load was very much lighter than in London, and the nights were undisturbed except, perhaps, by the strange rhythm of the beating of drums at some native festival.

One of the strangest reactions was to the climate. Each day the sun rose to its meridian and shone from a cloudless sky until sunset and the sudden onset of night. It was indeed true to say, in scriptural terms, that "the cloudless sky maketh the desert", and the sight of clouds and a good shower of British rain would have been most welcome.

The eternal drought seemed to produce a psychological tension in many people and I was reminded of the play, *The Rains Came*. The play depicts the emotional response of the people of India to the onset of the monsoons after the dry season, and for the first time I could appreciate this remarkable response.

There was a great sensation of isolation in the desert, but visualization of the domestic and family situation at home was never far from mind. It was to diminish anxieties at home that I never mentioned that I was in contact with a rabid dog, since the incubation of the disease could be as short as six weeks or as long as two years, and such suspense would have produced very prolonged anxiety at home.

While writing these memoirs regarding the 82nd General Hospital, I had the quite extraordinary experience of reading the obituary, in the current issue of the *Daily Telegraph*, of a former patient of mine on whom I operated almost half a century ago.

He was a major who was severely injured by a land mine in Palestine. I was asked by the Director of Medical Services at Headquarters in Cairo if I would undertake his further treatment. Always interested and enthusiastic to accept a surgical challenge I readily agreed to undertake his case.

In due course he arrived by air at the Benina airstrip and was admitted to the hospital. It was obvious that he needed considerable reconstructive surgery and a special day was arranged for his operation. All went well at operation and his future looked bright. He had special care in the post operative period and one of the nurses (Q.A.R.N.S.) noted that he was complaining of muscle cramp. She notified one of my colleagues who was a graded surgeon and a captain in the R.A.M.C.

He was a young surgeon of great academic attainment and immediately he jumped to the conclusion that the patient was suffering from tetanus. He put his name on the Dangerously Ill List (D.I.L.), and unfortunately this was reported to G.H.Q. If he had been put on the Seriously Ill List (S.I.L.) and then transferred to the D.I.L. there would have been no problem. However, to be put directly on the D.I.L. is considered with great seriousness. When I saw the patient I found that he was suffering from tetany, a condition of muscle spasms but nothing whatever to do with tetanus. I transferred him back to the S.I.L. but the damage was done and all hell broke loose.

I had a signal that the patient's father, Sir Arthur Street (later to be Chairman of the Coal Board) was proceeding "air soonest" with civilian consultants from London. My Commanding Officer (Lt.-Col. John B. Neal) and I went out to meet them at Benina Airfield. When the Dakota touched down we met Sir Arthur who was accompanied by a surgeon who was well known to me but whom at this stage I had never met. His name was Frank D'Abreu and he had brought with him a colleague who was a bacteriologist at the Westminster Hospital.

By the time we saw the patient he had completely recovered and was sitting up in bed and looking very well. The position was one of anticlimax and it was difficult to know what to do. My colleagues at the hospital decided to have a party in which Sir Arthur and my two colleagues joined with enthusiasm. The following morning we dispatched the whole party to their Dakota back to England. Many years later I had the pleasure of inviting Frank D'Abreu to my valedictory seminar in Darlington.

There is in the Army a feeling of team spirit and of mutual respect so it was with mixed feelings that I received my second posting. I was pleased that after one year I was promoted Lieutenant-Colonel in charge of the Surgical Division in the 97th General Hospital in Salonica in northern Greece, but I was sorry to leave my colleagues at the 82nd General Hospital where the morale was so high.

GREECE

The first part of the journey to Greece was the reverse of that from Cairo to Benghazi. We travelled by desert convoy to Tobruk and the

78

rest of the journey by train to reach Port Said for embarkation. Surprisingly, the ship was comfortable and I was to learn that one of the main advantages of rank was that I had a cabin on the journey to the Piraeus.

The city of Athens was an astonishing and inspiring sight. The Acropolis with its monuments and amphitheatres was a look back 2,000 years into history. Even the apostle Paul sprang to life when I first walked over Mars Hill where he gave his special address. The Royal Palace, the gardens and even the surrounding arid hills completed the picture of Grecian antiquity and of a former civilization.

The journey to Salonica was also by sea but the standards of comforts were very different. After a few days in Athens I embarked on a dreadful old cargo boat. All the troops were accommodated in bunks in the cargo hold. The heat was stifling though an attempt to ventilate the hold was made by the use of a canvas funnel lowered into the hold. This was more of a gesture than a serious attempt to keep conditions tolerable.

On arrival at Salonica I was met by the sergeant-major who escorted

FIGURE 5. *The author (centre) and officers of the 97th General Hospital in Salonica.*

me through the antiquated city of Salonica to my new unit. As we travelled through the city one could discern the boundary marks of the great fire that had decimated the city a quarter of a century previously. Strangely enough, there was a feeling of welcome in Greece which I found both surprising and pleasant. Though a rather arid country, Greece at first sight was green and verdant with its olive groves, which was in marked contrast to the desert of North Africa. The sight of European people who were friendly and so well disposed to the British troops was indeed a heart warming experience.

The hospital was in two parts, one housing the Medical Division in an old civilian hospital called the Hirsch Hospital, while the Surgical Division was housed about one mile away (Fig. 5). I took over the division from Lieutenant-Colonel Harold Burge who was later to establish a great reputation in London in the surgical treatment of duodenal ulcer. The surrounding territory in northern Greece was the 4th Division where there were stationed many famous Regiments including the 17/21 Lancers.

Two of the officers of my surgical division were to attain great distinction in later years. Captain Cyril Scurr,* the anaesthetist was to become one of the leading figures in the development of this speciality. The other was Captain Lloyd-Roberts,† R.A.M.C., a surgeon who worked with Fitzroy MacLean's team behind the enemy lines on the island of Viz, and an account of his work is told in the book, *Island of Terrible Friends*.[11]

He was an ebullient Old Etonian who had a great zest for life. He was a general surgeon who moved into orthopaedics and became Consultant Orthopaedic Surgeon at St. George's Hospital London. His daughter, Sue Lloyd-Roberts has attained a great reputation as a BBC television reporter. While he was working in my surgical division in the 97th General Hospital Lloyd Roberts would only on rare occasions refer to his service in the Army. Apparently, while working behind the German lines in Yugoslavia, he turned combatant and was, I believe, awarded several Yugoslavian decorations.

---

* C. F. Scurr C.B.E., L.V.O., Consultant Anaesthetist, Westminster Hospital, London
† George Lloyd Roberts F.R.C.S., Consultant Orthopaedic Surgeon, St. George's Hospital and Great Ormond Street Hospital.

FIGURE 6. *Greco–Roman remains destroyed by the Vandals. The origin of vandalism.*

During service in Greece I had to do various jobs all at the same time; as Officer-in-Charge of the Surgical Division, Officer Commanding the hospital, and as Assistant Director of Medical Services, (A.D.M.S.) to the 4th Division. This combined duty was referred to as wearing different hats and sometimes all these hats had to be worn at the same time.

The flexibility of my duties enabled me to travel freely in the Northern Command in Greece. I was able to visit many sites of historical and religious interest in Macedonia and Thrace. In particular I enjoyed the visits of Brigadier Elliott-Smith* who was the Command Consultant in surgery. He was the son of an Oxford professor and was an excellent Latin and Greek Scholar. We visited many sites in northern Greece

---

* Brigadier Elliott Smith, Command Consultant N.E.F., Consultant Surgeon, Radcliffe Hospital, Oxford.

where he was able to read the inscriptions of stones made in Greek or Roman times. Reading the inscriptions on the stones was difficult because part of the inscription was on one stone but the rest was on another stone separated by a wide distance.

The Vandals who overran this area centuries after the Greco-Roman period were reputed not to leave one stone on top of another and if this is so they certainly did their job well in northern Greece (Fig. 8). We visited the site where Mark Anthony and Brutus had their famous contest at Philippi, and also visited the place where St. Paul landed in Greece near Kavalla. Salonica (Thessaloniki) was itself one of the early centres of Christianity to which Paul wrote his famous Epistle to the Thessalonians.

Monasteries and religious shrines are usually situated on a mountain or on an island and in this respect Greece is no exception. Stretching down from Macedonia into the Aegean Sea there are three long fingers of land, the peninsulas of Athos, Longos and Kasandra.

Towards the tip of the most easterly peninsula there is a high and very attractive mountain, Mount Athos, rising steeply to over 6,000 feet.

Though Athos is in reality a peninsula the complete absence of roads means that it can only be approached by the sea so that for all practical purposes it is an island. It is, therefore, referred to as the Island of Athos. The geography provides the ideal site for the building of monasteries and there are twenty monasteries, some perched on the precipitous cliffs of this peninsula (Fig. 7). Athos is regarded as a holy mountain and is in an independent state controlled by a synod of twenty members, one from each of the monasteries. They do not adhere to central European time but follow solar time and sundials are seen everywhere in place of clocks. No females, human or animal are allowed on this island which really is a peninsula.

The Commanding Officer of the 4th Division in Greece (General Palmer) was anxious to encourage expeditions and I was offered either a climb of Mount Olympus or a visit to Athos. As I have no head for heights I chose the latter.

With about seven officers and non-commissioned officers we started from Salonica in jeeps in the early morning to travel to Stavros on the Gulf of Strimon. The roads in Macedonia were indescribably bad and were more like dried river beds than roads. Journeys were measured by

FIGURE 7. *The monastery at Vedapedi on Athos.*

time taken and not by distance. Unfortunately, we broke a spring in one of our jeeps and had to replace it. This was a long and exhausting task in very hot weather. Suffering fatigue and thirst, we arrived at the little fishing village of Stavros where Greek fishermen were waiting to take us on our sea journey to Athos.

We embarked late in the afternoon on the strange looking fishing craft so common in Greece and which is called a caique. The prow and the stern of the vessel were high but the middle of the vessel had a low freeboard so that the deck was almost level with the sea. The weather was calm and progress was good and as the evening drew on the sun began to set and we could see the mountain of Athos surrounded by a sunlit coronet of cloud, while our ship was enveloped in darkness. I realized from this sight why the mountain was considered sacred.

It was long after dark when we arrived at Vadapedi where the monastery was situated on the side of the cliff (Fig. 7). The night was fine and some of us decided to sleep on deck, but about five of us went to stay in the monastery. After considerable formalities with the prior we were at last admitted by the monks, who were all dressed in the official habit of the Greek Orthodox Church (Fig. 8). We were received in audience by the Prior and Members of the Order. Exhausted with the journey and by thirst we were revived by the Greek liqueur Ouzo, a drink

FIGURE 8. *The Prior of the monastery at Vedapedi on Athos.*

which we found more intoxicating than thirst quenching. The Prior told us stories of British prisoners of war who escaped from the German prison camps and sought refuge in the monastery. One of these escapees apparently took ill at the monastery and died of what was thought to be malaria. In great detail the Prior told us of his fate and then proceeded to give a clear description of the symptoms which the escapee had suffered and which were typical of typhus rather than of malaria.

Later on, after going down into the cellars to sleep on old mattresses, I found that the mattresses were lice infested. Immediately I realized that the escapee had not died of malaria but of lice-borne typhus. I knew that even though one was infested with infected lice, the infection was only transmitted by scratching. It was indeed most difficult not to scratch, so little sleep was possible in that long night. In the morning the cellars looked out over a sunlit bay and I was dying of thirst and of headache as the result of drinking Ouzo. The monastic rule was that there was to be no eating or drinking before the sun was over the meridian. The morning did indeed seem long and when at last midday arrived we were given a meal of fruit and fish. I had longed for a long soft drink but was given more Ouzo.

After a day or two of inspection of the monastery and reviewing what remaining treasures it possessed after years of neglect, we travelled to the next monastery at Lavra. This monastery was even more depressing

84

and it was difficult to realize that in the Middle Ages Athos was the centre of Greek learning and of Byzantine art. One day in Lavra was followed by our return journey on which we took some of the monks who were permitted on occasions to have relief from the monastic life.

Though the day was clear there was a tremendous swell and many of us were seasick. To see great waves approaching the caique with its low freeboard one felt that each wave would swamp the ship. Miraculously, the ship rose above the waves and one realized that the design and structure of the ship was the result of centuries of practical building experience.

In view of the danger of any of us developing louse-borne typhus our return to Salonica was marked by an immediate visit to the medical officer to have the routine inoculations against typhus.

Throughout the various travels in northern Greece there were two problems always present in my mind, one was military and the other one medical.

The military problems arose because of the political uncertainly in northern Greece. Communist gunmen, called the Andarte, were at large and attacked Greek Army units and police outposts with great ferocity and, being a purely guerrilla force were taking no prisoners. In spite of the fact that our K.D. uniforms were identical to those of the Greek Army we never came into any danger.

The second problem was medical and was related to malaria. In the Struma Valley the incidence of malaria was said to be the highest in the world. In the First World War more soldiers perished because of malaria in this terrain than from enemy action. In this area the malaria was particularly severe and was called cerebral malaria. The victim suddenly became unconscious and unless the cause of the coma was recognized and treated the outcome was fatal. Fortunately, because of prophylactic drug measures and the routine use of mosquito nets these disasters were avoided in most, but not all, units.

Human memory is selective and retains that which it wishes to re-member, and it was certainly true in my recollections of Greece. The visits to outlying medical units (First Aid Posts) with Brigadier Elliott-

Smith, were of great interest and the only private visit to Athos was fascinating.

It was, however, the work in the surgical division of the 97th General Hospital that occupied almost all my time. The work was mainly routine and there were few clinical highlights, though it was noticeable that administration was beginning to encroach on one's time.

The only case of special interest was a lieutenant-colonel of an infantry regiment who developed a strange thrombosis (clot) which blocked in the largest vein in the abdomen (the inferior vena cava) and whose legs and abdomen became immensely swollen. I had never seen nor indeed read about such a condition but decided to remove the clot from the abdominal vein. The result was dramatic and recovery was complete. Only once in recent experience have I seen this condition which occurred in one of my gynaecological colleagues who was desperately ill and underwent the same, very unusual, operation with a similar result.

It was towards the autumn when I first heard of my entitlement to home leave. This was a most exciting prospect since it was so long since I had seen Joan and our infant twins. Leave was to be for one month which seemed a most generous prospect.

HOME LEAVE – LILOP

Many soldiers on overseas postings had spent several years abroad without the opportunity of returning to the United Kingdom. To meet this situation a system of leave was introduced which was given a code name in typical army fashion. It was called LILOP which was translated as Leave in Lieu of Python. Whatever the code name, the leave was welcome and having obtained my official papers I went to the mud air strip outside Salonica and to emplane on the ubiquitous Dakota transport plane *en route* to Athens. Colonel Barry, the Commanding Officer of the hospital in Salonica had been posted to Athens and had forgotten to take his colonel's red hat. He sent a signal to me asking me that when I went on leave would I bring his hat to Athens. Accordingly I was carrying his red hat on my kit bag when some of my friends teased me that I had been promoted to full colonel. After all there is said to be a field-marshal's baton in every private's knapsack.

During the overnight stay in Athens I met the pilot who was to fly me home on leave. He was a charming squadron leader called Hodge. At this time, so different from today, the pilot could choose his own route home. He asked me what way I would like to go and, as I was anxious to see as much of southern Greece as possible, it was decided we should fly over the Gulf of Corinth, over the toe of Italy and to stay overnight in Rome.

After take off from Hassani airport (Athens) he invited me to travel in the co-pilots seat. I found this fascinating and, as we flew at low altitude, in the clear weather there was visibility for 50 miles. The straight line of the Corinth Canal with its high clear-cut walls was most impressive and acted as a line to divide southern Greece into a northern and a southern part.

Over the Corinth Canal I was to see for the first time the automatic pilot which was called George, and the radar altimeter, a brilliant British invention. It was remarkable to see the aircraft flying without a hand on the controls but the most remarkable thing was the use of the radar altimeter.

The ordinary altimeter measures the height of the aircraft above sea level so it would be possible to fly into a mountain side. The radar altimeter is different in that it focuses on the land in front and takes away the danger of collisions in low visibility. It was most interesting to fly along the Gulf of Corinth and to approach an island on automatic pilot. The aircraft, as it approached the island, automatically rose over the top of the island and then down the other side.

Squadron Leader Hodge told me that this device was used on our torpedo aircraft at the battle of Matapan. Our aircraft flew in at low altitude to attack the Italian battleships, and were able to fire their torpedoes and then automatically to climb higher without colliding with the super structure of the ships. This caused consternation in the Italian Navy.

Flying at relatively low altitudes provides a panoramic view which is seldom encountered by the high-flying jets of today. And so it was that after a most interesting flight we approached Rome. Looking ahead to the narrow pencil of the runway it seemed impossible to land on this narrow strip, but as we approached the strip became wider and longer and we made a perfect three point landing.

An early morning take off from Rome and a Mediterranean flight took us over the Isle of Elba and the northern tip of Corsica to land at Istres, an aerodrome situated on the mouth of the River Rhône near Marseilles, and having the longest runway that I had ever seen. From Istres we flew over the great mountainous area of the Massif Central to pass west of Paris and to see the welcome sight of the English Channel.

With every mile my excitement at coming home mounted, coming to a crescendo when we landed at Blackbush. I remember little of the journey to London but remember making my way to our home at South Park Hill Road in Croydon. Joan looked as pretty as ever and our twin sons were getting quite large and beginning to walk and to talk. The reunion after such a long time was idyllic and emotional.

In prospect a month seemed such a long time, but the time vanished and soon I had to report to Blackbush R.A.F. Station for the journey back to Greece.

The weather at this time was terrible and the passengers few. All of us were posted "air soonest" so the flight could not be postponed for better weather. There were an admiral, a captain and a lieutenant-commander in the Royal Navy who formed a special group on their way to Athens. I was informed that they were to fly out to join the Mediterranean Fleet in the Adriatic Sea. It was at a time just before the British destroyer was mined near Corfu. Later on I was to conclude that the urgency of our visit was to do with the "Corfu incident".

The other four passengers were, the Chief of C.I.D., the Chief Engineer of Greece, an archaeologist and myself. The weather forecasts over Europe were terrible but for all our group the journey was urgent and so we took off again in a Dakota. I can still see the W.A.A.F. officer close the aircraft door and standing in pouring rain wave us goodbye. Through a break in the clouds I saw that we were passing over Eastbourne, but that was the last sight of land for many anxious hours. At first there was an arrogance about the naval staff who using their ranks chose the best seats on the aircraft. These seats had been taken out and fitted facing backwards to increase safety in bad weather. As the nightmare journey progressed the naval arrogance got less and less as these professional sailors, one by one, became airsick.

As we reached the mountainous area of the Massif Central in southern France the journey was dark and terrifying. I felt that the wings of the aircraft would be ripped off by the storm. After an hour or so the plane seemed to drop out of the sky and suddenly the cloud cleared and we were in a mountainous valley roofed in by cloud. The pilot circled round the valley just above the tops of a pine forest as he looked for a way out of the dilemma. To climb into cloud would be at risk of running into the sides of the mountain and there seemed to be no solution to the problem.

After some consideration a river valley was located and flying up this valley the Dakota once again climbed into cloud and into the darkness. The vision of crashing into the mountain was ever present and disaster seemed inevitable.

However, after what seemed an eternity of terror, we broke cloud cover and there was a sigh of relief from the seven passengers. It was at this time that the pilot, an R.A.F. squadron leader, came through and announced that the journey south had to be abandoned and we were running low in fuel. He considered that we could make Bordeaux with the help of a following wind. The admiral, as senior officer, whose arrogance had now all evaporated, readily agreed and we turned west-ward.

As we set our course for the emergency landing we progressively lost height but by great good fortune reached Bordeaux and landed on the grass without a formal approach and with one engine cut out.

Grounded by bad weather for two days at Bordeaux we were accom-modated in a little inn, which five years later I tried, unsuccessfully, to locate. The quiet safety of being on the ground convinced me that I should never fly again. However, the weather improved and we again took off on our flight two days later. We flew in the first instance to Istres where we re-fuelled and took off with the intention of landing at Rome. However, on this occasions, due to the light passenger load of only seven officers, we were able to fly direct to Greece and to land at Athens.

Winter comes suddenly in northern Greece. When I went on leave the weather was fine and sunny but on my return to Salonica the skies were grey, the clouds were low and there was a bitterly cold north wind. It was a time for battle dress and great coats.

I was very surprised to be met by a captain in the surgical division who was not particularly well known to me. He welcomed me and escorted me to the hospital where a little reunion party had been arranged.

It was with inner satisfaction that I realized the loyalty of my colleagues and that while on leave I had not been forgotten. I was reminded of a story about an ancient church in London's dockland which had been in ruins for years except for the spire. When the London County Council decided to demolish the entire building there was an outcry from a very unexpected quarter. The pilots of the Thames Port Authority were very upset since they had, unknown to everybody, been taking bearings on the spire for many years and the loss of the landmark to them alone was great. The influence of people and the value of things are often only appreciated after they have gone.

It seemed strange to be back at work in a foreign country but as so often happens, within a few days one felt that one had never been away. In the few clear days that came along from time to time the snow-capped tip of Mount Olympus could be seen, a reminder of the onset of winter. In the grey days and with a cold northern wind blowing down from the mountains, the prospect of a winter of military hospital work was uninspiring.

Then quite unexpectedly a posting came through and I became quite excited. The appointment was that of Officer-in-Charge of the surgical division of the 19th General Hospital which was a very large command hospital in the Suez Canal Zone. I confessed to being delighted to being promoted to the then senior surgical post in the Middle East but sad at the prospect of leaving Greece. During service in Greece I had been very impressed by the Greek people and had come to regard them with respect and affection. From the Greek peasants scratching out a living in the arid mountains round Kozani, to the professional and business people of Salonica, I found them courageous and loyal.

Leaving the cold of Salonica in battle dress and wearing a great coat and to arrive in the heat of Athens made one realize that the climate of Greece north of Volos is very different from that in southern Greece. But even the heat of Athens was nothing to that experienced when the plane landed on a airstrip in the Suez Canal Zone. Once again one had to return to the tropical kit that one had worn for the past two years.

EGYPT

The nineteenth General Hospital was the largest in the Middle East and was situated on the Suez Canal at Fayid about the mid point between Port Said on the Mediterranean in the north and Suez on the Red Sea in the south. The canal was said to be 90 miles long, 90 yards wide and 90 years old, and had a key strategic importance.

The hospital was close to the Great Bitter Lake and the word bitter was a reference to its high salt content, a feature reflected by its great buoyancy to the swimmer. It was located on the desert sand on a strip of land between a range of two arid hills and the lake itself. The larger hill was called the "flea" and the lesser hill the "little flea". At anchor in the Bitter Lake there were two large Italian battleships, memorials to the surrender of Italy and the breakup of the German-Italian Axis.

The hospital was a very large one and was accommodated in huts and in tents. All major specialties were included as this was the "command" hospital. The medical division was commanded by Lieutenant-Colonel Anderson (son of Sir John Anderson, the then Home Secretary) and I was in command of the surgical division.

I can not speak too highly of the surgical specialists in my division but would mention Major Douglas Freebody[*] who was the orthopaedic specialist and who did outstanding work, especially on soldiers who suffered from prolapsed discs. Major Philip Reading[†] of the London Hospital was our E.N.T. specialist and was a good colleague. My own anaesthetist, Major Robert Stout,[‡] was the first to use the new relaxant drug, curare, which was such a major advance in anaesthesia. This facilitated surgical procedures by producing relaxation of the muscles without the patient having to be deeply anaesthetized. This use of curare, which is allied to arrow poison, increased the safety, scope and success in abdominal surgery, is now a major feature of modern anaesthesia.

In the hospital the clinical work was especially interesting since it dealt, not only with British service personnel, but also with the German

[*] Douglas Freebody, F.R.C.S., Consultant Orthopaedic Surgeon, Kingston & Richmond Health Authority.
[†] Philip Reading, M.S., F.R.C.S., Consultant E.N.T. Surgeon, Guy's Hospital.
[‡] Robert Stout, Consultant Anaesthetist, Medway Health District

prisoners of war who were accommodated in camps nearby, and with over 90,000 displaced civilians. The surgical work, in consequence, began to turn away from purely military surgery with its limited scope, to the wider fields of civilian practice. There was no air conditioning in the operating theatres so we started work very early in the morning and after the midday break resumed our work in the evening.

My batman, who was a German prisoner of war called Richard, worked with a care and diligence far exceeding anything I had ever experienced with British soldiers. From him I learned a great deal about the German character and of the prisoner of war camps that surrounded our hospital. In each camp the prisoners were graded A, B, C1 and C2. The category A referred to anti-Nazi, the B, to Germans and the C, were Nazis while those in category C2 were probably war criminals. Even in captivity the grading was apparent and loyalty between each group was often missing.

On one occasion I operated on an Austrian officer who in civilian life was a judge. He had a gall bladder disease and was operated on under routine general anaesthesia. I was surprised to find that two days later he was put under arrest as a war criminal.

I can only presume that when recovering from his anaesthetic he talked and let out secrets which were overheard by the German military order-lies who had made a report resulting in his arrest. He was subsequently on a charge of executing prisoners of war in Nazi Germany, but before he came to trial I had been posted home on release. He wrote to me years later to tell me that he had been acquitted and was back in his legal practice in Vienna.

It was during this appointment at the 19th General Hospital that I realized the importance of clinical administration, where organization of work was always relative to the patient's welfare and not for administrative convenience as we see so often today in the Health Service. I realized, also, the importance of Theatre Operating Teams which were not subject to constant change on the illegitimate excuse of staff training.

From military Standing Orders I also realized the importance of treatment routines which were issued to all the Queen Alexander Nursing officers as well as to officers in the Royal Army Medical Corps. These orders formed the basis of the ward management of surgical cases and left no doubt in the minds of the medical and nursing staff as to how to handle a wide variety of surgical treatments.

Years later after discharge from the service I re-arranged these orders in the form of a booklet which I issued to all my Units. It came to be known as The Surgical Bible and went through several editions as the management of cases evolved with each surgical advance. These three features of organization, the formation of Theatre Teams and the ward procedures formed the basis of the philosophy which I followed throughout my entire surgical career.

The year spent at work in this large hospital was a year well spent. On my only local leave I went to Port Said, a town where east and west seemed to intermingle in a natural way.

Sitting on the balcony of the officers club one could watch the great ships sail through the Suez Canal. This was the gateway from the Mediterranean to India and to the Far East. I had often wished to go to the Far East and as I watched the ships sail south I could picture future adventures in this part of the world.

It was at this officers club, too, that I met some Americans who were reluctant to pay tribute to the influence of the British in Egypt. They seemed anxious to play a bigger part in Middle Eastern politics and to displace the British and to replace British experience with American influence. In the event the British were displaced after the Suez War but this left a vacuum in this area which was soon to be the scene of the war between Israel and Egypt and all the consequences that were to follow.

At this time the Director of Medical Services in the Middle East was a most charming Major-General who was known as "Jock" Munro. He had remained the most eligible bachelor in the army for many years but had recently been married. He described himself as "a poacher turned gamekeeper", and I am sure that this was a correct description. We got on very well together and he asked me if I would be interested in becoming Consultant Surgeon to South East Asia Command (S.E.A.C.), a post with the rank of brigadier.

It was a tempting offer since I had always wanted to visit the Far East and reports from my friends in London told of uncertainty of professional life and job prospects back in England. However, the thoughts of family at home were too strong and I decided to return home on completion of my military service in what was called the Age and Service Group.

It was with some sadness that I handed over my unit to my successor and said goodbye to all my friends and started on my journey home which was to be my last service adventure. I joined another group of soldiers due home on release, who were assembled in the Canal Zone.

We emplaned on a York transport plane which really was a Lancaster bomber adapted for troop carrying. We took off early in the morning and flew to El Adam near Tobruk and then on to Benina which was an airstrip near Benghazi where I had my first posting at the 82nd General Hospital. We staged at Tripoli before crossing the Mediterranean to make a further stop at Istres.

Among the service passengers there were several R.A.F. officers of very high rank. Throughout this part of the flight they went forward to take over the controls and I felt that our own pilot got very fed up with this procession of group captains and air commodores upsetting his normal routine. This interruption continued throughout the flight.

We crossed over France uneventfully and it was night time as we approached R.A.F. Lineham. As we came in to land I seemed to realize that we were travelling too fast and that we were going to overshoot the runway. I had felt all along that the pilot had been thoroughly irritated with the constant interruptions from senior officers.

My suspicions that we were going to overshoot the runway were fully justified and this indeed proved to be the case. After bouncing along the tarmac with heavy braking it was obvious that we could not stop and the pilot decided to take off again. There were a few seconds of juddering which seemed like an eternity while the aircraft attempted to gain speed and height.

At last we were again airborne but apparently with some damage to the undercarriage. I looked at my watch and it was 10.20 p.m. and I noted that we were circling round and round the air field. Looking down I could see the lights of fire engines and ambulances as they were assembling near the runway. It was a most frightening sensation to feel that those below us were preparing for an air crash.

At long last we came in for our attempted landing. This indeed proved to be the worst landing that I have ever experienced and as we careered along the runway fire engines and ambulances pursued us until we finally came to a halt. A large number of R.A.F. personnel clamoured to open the doors of the aircraft and to get us out. I presume there was some danger of fire and all of us were very frightened.

Back at the R.A.F. mess, as we were being restored by a full glass of whisky, one of the air commodores said to the pilot, "you gave us a terrible fright". "Yes," said the pilot, "and I did not enjoy it any more than you did."

That night I shared a room with a major who was in the Royal Artillery. At about 4 a.m. he began to scream and shout and I presume that he was ab-reacting to the terrifying experience. I gave him a sedative and we both went off to sleep.

When I awoke in the morning I looked out of the window and saw two swans swimming quietly across a pond with a dignity that only swans possess. I felt that this was a better method of transport and this renewed my resolve made in Bordeaux during our forced landing, that I would never fly again. The thought of being killed while flying home on release was too much to contemplate.

11

Home Coming

THE great joy of coming home was to some extent marred by political
and professional uncertainty. The people were exhausted by war
and years of rationing, while the profession was in a state of turbulence
and uncertainty. The seeds sown in Cronin's book *The Citadel*, had taken
root in the minds of the politicians and a National Health Service act
was being discussed.

In the pursuit of nationalization in all its forms and of nationalized
medicine in particular, Aneurin Bevan and his socialist colleagues saw
political power and fame at a single stroke. I had noted in the Army
Education Corps a strong left-wing tendency, and I have no doubt that
this influenced the general election that resulted in Churchill being
deposed in spite of his outstanding statesmanship and leadership during
the war.

Certainly, many servicemen looked to socialism for the security it
appeared to offer instead of the uncertainties they had encountered in
service life. It was natural that they were inclined to the left and welcomed
the concept of a National Health Service as part of a Welfare State in
which all the needs of each citizen would be met, and everyone would
be looked after from birth to death, as outlined in the Beveridge Report.

In the medical profession there was much turmoil and uncertainty.
The British Medical Association and the Royal Colleges were not in
agreement and in this scenario of professional dissension the politicians
were not slow to exploit the situation. The medico-political events of
this time are brilliantly exposed by Sir Reginald Murley (a former
President of the Royal College of Surgeons of England) in his book,
Surgical Roots and Branches.[12]

In short, the N.H.S. proposed that after the state takeover there was to be no buying and selling of practices. Practitioners who had bought their practices were not to be compensated until they retired but their relatives would receive benefit if they died before retirement. In the meantime they were to receive a niggardly interest on the capital involved.

On the other hand, the specialist hospital doctors were to be offered a full time salary in the National Health Service. This proposal certainly favoured the consultant members of the profession, and tended to drive a wedge between the consultants and the general practitioners. The service to the patient was to be free at the time of their need and that the population was to be cared for from "womb to tomb".

After much acrimonious discussion with the B. M. A. and many secret meetings between individual members of the profession and the politicians, the N.H.S. was finally launched in 1948. There were honours and awards for those in the profession who supported the Government line.

During these uncertain years I decided that I could not influence events and would devote all my energies to my ambition to continue my career in surgery though at this time the prospects were bleak. The first problem was to obtain a consultant appointment but this presented many problems.

There were very many specialists who had been discharged from the services at a time when new appointments were held up because of the imminent introduction of the National Health Service. It was a time, too, when established consultants were applying for new consultant appointments and competing for them against their own registrars.

On one occasion I was short listed for two appointments and had to attend the Headquarters of the North West Metropolitan Board in Portland Place, when one interview was in the morning and the other was in the afternoon. At the morning interview a senior surgeon who was well known to me was acting as Surgical Assessor on myself and the other candidates. In the afternoon I met him again but on this second occasion he himself was an applicant for the post that I too was seeking.

Many years previously, and just before the war, I had attended a course in surgery at the Royal College of Surgeons in Edinburgh.

I was greatly impressed by the teaching of a young surgeon, Ian Aird.

After the war he was appointed Professor of Surgery at the Postgraduate Medical School at Hammersmith Hospital where he succeeded Professor Grey Turner.

Professor Grey Turner who was formerly Professor of Surgery at Newcastle-upon-Tyne, came to Hammersmith Hospital as the first Professor of Surgery at the Postgraduate Medical School. He was the first of a long series of very distinguished Professors of Surgery including Professor R. B. Welbourn* who made such outstanding contributions to endocrinology. I went to see Professor Aird who had himself just returned from service in the Royal Army Medical Corps. After discussion he appointed me Senior Registrar and subsequently assistant Lecturer in Surgery.

I was his first assistant for five years, during which time I came to know him well. Before he came to London and while he was in Edinburgh he wrote surgical notes for the candidates for the Fellowship examination. These notes were short and excellent and were know as Aird's Notes.

Copies of his notes were difficult to obtain and fetched very high prices when passed from one Fellowship candidate to another. While at Hammersmith he re-wrote and expanded these notes which were published as a famous text book, *Companion in Surgical Studies*.[13] It was a most comprehensive book and did not contain a single diagram or picture which was quite unique in surgical text books.

I had the honour of helping him in some ways towards its production. He used to ask me to obtain reprints of all the leading articles on a subject such as breast tumours. I would assemble these and prepare them for his review. He would take these to his study and distil the contents of dozens of surgical papers into a single chapter. It was an intellectual feat of great merit by a single author.

Most successful books on surgery are followed soon by a reprint or by a second edition. Aird's book was indeed reprinted in 1950 and the second edition appeared in 1957. After his untimely death no other author or authors have had the temerity to produce a third edition until last year when a successor to Aird's book appeared.

Other than as a writer and teacher Aird's interests were in research.

---

* Prof R. B. Welbourn, D.Sc., M.D., F.R.C.S., Emeritus Professor of Surgery, Royal Post-Graduate School and Hammersmith Hospital, London.

He envisaged the possibility of organ transplants and with the help of the staff at the Buxton and Browne Research Department of the Royal College of Surgeons at Downe in Kent, a kidney transplant was performed. The transplanted kidney was sited in the neck of a dog.

This famous greyhound was shown and discussed at many meetings throughout the country. It was perhaps one of the earliest clinical signposts on the road to routine renal transplants such as we have today.

In actual fact, though the transplanted kidney at first worked well, as time went on it was rejected and though it continued to secrete, the fluid was not real urine as the kidney had lost its proper function, and could produce only water.

Perhaps the most important contribution to surgery was Aird's concept of an artificial heart. He selected a brilliant young research registrar called Dennis Melrose to work on this project. Melrose had a genius for invention and innovation and started work in a research room in a Nissen hut at Hammersmith Hospital. The earliest models of the artificial heart were crude "Heath Robinson" affairs which were clumsy and involved passing air over a great lake of blood, so that the blood could be oxygenated.

One morning Melrose arrived delighted with a great new idea to facilitate this blood oxygenation. He had seen his wife cut up eggs to make a salad and it occurred to him that if he could use an apparatus with multiple parallel blades like the egg cutter he could then rotate them through a sump of blood and thereby produce a vast surface for oxygenation in a very confined space. This was a major space saving mechanism and a great advance. Moreover, it became apparent that the transit of blood must be pulsatile and not simply by pressure delivery. Accordingly pulsating hammers were introduced into the pump system which was to become more and more efficient as time went on.

The only role that I played in this was a clinical one. During my experience in the London blitz and in the army I had performed a very great number of amputations.

In view of this experience, Aird asked me to do all the leg amputations in the unit. In doing so I was to identify the blood vessels of the limb and, especially also, the sciatic nerve.

As soon as the limb was removed in the operating theatre it went straight down to Melrose's laboratory where the arteries and veins were attached to the artificial heart. In this way that part of the leg which was viable was kept alive. In addition, electrical stimulation of the sciatic nerve was carried out and this made the leg twitch which confirmed the survival of the muscle structure. Melrose's success laid the foundation of modern heart surgery and in due course he was promoted to a well deserved Professorial chair.

The fact that a mechanical artificial heart was invented enabled surgeons to stop the patients heart and to operate on the damaged heart while the patient's circulation was maintained by what came to be known as the Melrose pump. Heart valves could, therefore, be repaired or replaced and in more modern times heart transplants performed.

To Ian Aird and to Dennis Melrose the greatest credit is due for laying the foundation and basis of modern heart surgery. From this crude beginning the modern artificial heart has developed and is now efficient and compact, and its use has opened up a whole new world in cardiac surgery.

In spite of the academic erudition I found that I had little to learn in operative surgery from any of the consultant staff at Hammersmith Hospital with the exception of R. H. (Dick) Franklin who was an experienced and practical surgeon. I felt, therefore, that I should engage in a research project and was encouraged to do so by Ian Aird.

In view of my experience of peptic ulcer while doing Harold Edwards' clinic at King's College Hospital, I felt that my project should be related to duodenal and gastric ulcers.

Since the First World War great emphasis was placed on the importance of excessive acidity in producing these ulcers and a wide variety of test meals to assess gastric acidity were carried out. On passing tubes into the stomach samples of gastric juice were obtained and the acidity measured. It was found that in duodenal ulcer the acidity was high but in gastric ulcer the acidity was normal or low.

I had myself, however, encountered several cases of duodenal ulcer with complete absence of acid (achlorhydria) in the stomach. It occurred to me that acidity itself was not the primary cause of the problem but that it was more likely that the action of a digestive ferment called pepsin caused the damage. I therefore embarked on a research programme to estimate the peptic activity of the gastric juice in duodenal and in gastric ulcer.

The technique of estimations then was prolonged and cumbersome and, with inadequate laboratory assistance, very time consuming. After a period of four years' work I had made what I thought was an important discovery. In duodenal ulcer where the gastric acidity was high (pH 2.1), peptic activity was at its peak. On the other hand, in gastric ulcer where the ulcer was in the stomach itself, the acidity was normal or low at a pH of 3.9 and at this point peptic action was at its maximum.

It occurred to me that there were two different "pepsins" working at different acidities. Should a patient possess both these pepsins he would be a candidate for combined duodenal and gastric ulcer, a condition which occurred in about five per cent of patients.

Accordingly, I prepared a thesis based on this work and submitted it to my old Medical School at Queen's University, Belfast. The thesis was rejected on the grounds that it did not conform to the views of the authorities predominating at this time.

It is interesting to note that Gregory, in Liverpool, fifteen years later described two pepsins, one working at a pH of 2.1 and the other at a pH of 3.8 which was just the very point that I had made fifteen years previously. It is apparently important not to be in advance of your time or indeed of your university!

While working at the London Postgraduate Medical School I came more fully to recognize the importance of the Fellowship of the Royal College of Surgeons, England. While the Edinburgh Fellowship was appropriate north of the Tweed and was respected throughout the world, in the Metropolis the English Fellowship was essential. In the academic atmosphere at the Postgraduate Medical School at Hammersmith Hospital it was easy to study and so I started working for the Primary examination in anatomy and physiology.

As I had been a part-time demonstrator in anatomy at King's College, Strand, the Primary was not, I thought, likely to present any problems except perhaps the risk of ill fortune at the actual examination.

There were two brother professors called Harris, one who examined in anatomy and the other in physiology. The record of these professors in failing candidates was infamous. It was said that if you encountered one of these professors in your examination your chances of passing were slim but if you encountered both the position was hopeless. I had the great misfortune to encounter both but in spite of this misfortune passed the examination.

I sat the next available Final examination without even opening a textbook in surgery. The written and clinical examinations were no problem but in the surgical oral examination an unexpected confrontation was to occur.

In the oral Fellowship examinations there are two examiners, one who asks the questions and the other who carries out the marking. I was examined by two famous London surgeons, Hanfield Jones* from St. Mary's Hospital and Clive Butler† from the London Hospital.

With Hanfield Jones I had some disagreement about a case of syphilitic bursitis but as he had very special experience of this condition a truce was declared. He then produced a specimen of the condition known as congenital dislocation of the hip and said, "what is that, *boy?*" Having just retired from the services as a lieutenant-colonel in charge of the largest surgical division in the British Army I was incensed at this disrespect. However, as I had worked closely with Lambrinudi, the Senior Orthopaedic Surgeon at Guy's and had dealt with dozens of cases of congenital dislocation of the hip at the Queen Mary's Hospital, Car-shalton, I felt that I was at an advantage and that the tables were turned. When I was describing the condition Hanfield Jones kept interrupting me and I got more and more annoyed and finally said firmly, "Sir, if you will listen I will tell you all *you* need to know about this condition!"

He was stunned into silence at once but even his silence and his attitude reminded me of the charge that we used to make against soldiers who adopted an air of dumb insolence and this made me even more annoyed. However he recovered his own composure enough to ask me how to reduce the dislocation.

I started my answer in a controlled rage by saying, "first of all you forget all that rubbish that you read in surgical textbooks and then you manipulate the dislocation as follows." I then described in words and mime how to carry out the procedure.

There was a deathly silence and then suddenly I realized that he and

---

* Hanfield Jones, M.S., F.R.C.S., Consultant Surgeon, St. Mary's Hospital, London.
† Clive Butler, F.R.C.S., Consultant Surgeon, The London Hospital.

Sir Arthur Porritt* had just published a new textbook in surgery.[14] The cause of the silence was all too clear. Then Clive Butler took over with charm and tact asking me a few emollient questions, the answers to these being all to obvious. I felt sure that Hanfield Jones would fail me, his whole attitude being quite offensive, and I had been politely aggressive.

The results of the Final Fellowship are made known in the hall of the Royal College in Lincoln's Inn Fields. The candidates assemble and are called by an officer of the College to the foot of an elegant stairway. If you have passed the examination you ascended the stairway to meet the members of Council but if you fail you slink back into the crowd and are absorbed.

I remember crossing the Hall with great trepidation and could think of nothing but the unpleasant encounter with Hanfield Jones. Arriving at the bottom of the stairs, I was informed that I had passed the examination and was permitted to go upstairs to meet the members of Council. As I ascended the stairs I wondered what Hanfield Jones would say, but I cannot remember meeting him again then or ever.

In later years I was to learn from some of my colleagues who were examiners for the Fellowship that Hanfield Jones was often asked, much to his embarrassment, "who was that chap with the strange name who took the mickey out of you at the Fellowship examination?"

While at Hammersmith Hospital I met Professor Grey Turner whose name, for me, was a legend. For a year or two after he retired and had handed over to Ian Aird he lingered in the wards talking to his old friends and his ward sisters. He was a quiet man who wore a dark jacket and striped trousers.

Aird had at this time asked me to prepare a paper on fluid balance and intravenous infusions in surgical patients.

I worked for six months on this project and then made a scientific presentation which came to the conclusion that the average patient requires one bottle of saline and two bottles of water in twenty-four hours. Grey Turner saw this paper lying on sister's desk and having

---

* Sir Arthur Porritt, Formerly President of The Royal College of Surgeons of England.

looked it through simply remarked, "I could have told you that years ago." I felt that I had wasted my time.

Grey Turner was a surgical genius whose work was known all over the world but who never received any civil decoration or lay recognition of his eminence. His citation for knighthood was, I am told, not supported by the then President of the Royal College of Surgeons of England. The president's name is long forgotten but the name of Grey Turner lives on.

It was as a general surgeon that Grey Turner showed a special interest in cancer of the oesophagus (gullet). While in Newcastle he told me he was often criticized because of the high mortality of his early efforts at oesophagectomy (removal of the gullet).

At a later date his former detractors were all too willing to share his glory and his success when he became famous at the Postgraduate Medical School.

At this time, too, I was able to meet Grey Turner's second in command, R. H. (Dick) Franklin. * Franklin was an outstanding surgeon of great skill and modesty and he, Ivor Lewis† of the North Middlesex Hospital, and Norman Tanner‡ at St. James Hospital, Balham, were to contribute enormously to the beginning of the surgical treatment of cancer of the oesophagus.

After just over five years at Hammersmith Hospital I had a great yearning to start my own unit and be free from any further influence of the surgical tradition of any medical school. Circumstances during the war had contrived to give me practical surgical experience in civil and in military life that was quite unique and unlikely ever to be repeated. To this experience, army discipline and training had provided a taste for administration. Working at the Postgraduate Medical School was to add a research and academic component to enable me to attain, by circumstances and good fortune, what I consider was quite a unique training and experience in surgery while still a young man.

---

* R. H. Franklin C.B.E., F.R.C.S., Senior Lecturer in Surgery at Hammersmith Hospital. Consultant Surgeon, Kingston Hospital.

† Ivor Lewis, M.S., Consultant Surgeon, North Middlesex.

‡ Norman Tanner M.S., F.R.C.S., Consultant Surgeon, St. James' Hospital, Balham, London.

Obtaining a suitable appointment was, however, by no means easy and in negotiating the various vicissitudes I learned much of the internal politics of the profession. This caused me much sadness and I realized that the best candidate did not always get the job, not because he was not good enough, but rather that he was too good and might cause a threat to the establishment. In Biblical phrase, "the race is not always to the swift or the battle to the strong."

12

Surgeon in the North

IN FORMER YEARS only London and the Provincial University cities had a full consultant service, though in large cities the local authority had hospitals staffed by full time medical officers. The rest of the country was served by Cottage Hospitals and by a series of War Memorial Hospitals which had been erected in memory of those who died in the First World War.

These hospitals were supported by voluntary subscription and were staffed by general practitioners. Some of the staff were Fellows of the Royal Colleges or held a Doctorate in Medicine of one of the universities, but much of their time was spent in general practice and it was from this source that most of their income was derived.

The appointments to the voluntary hospitals were honorary and un-paid. Inevitably, the standard of work lacked the expertise of fully qualified specialists all of whose time and energy were devoted to their work in surgery, medicine or obstetrics.

The advent of the National Health Service initiated radical changes in the hospital service. In each area existing hospitals were expanded or new hospitals built to provide a specialist service available to the patient at a local District General Hospital. Specialists who formerly were con-centrated centrally in the Teaching Hospitals were dispersed throughout the entire country to provide expertise to the District General Hospitals and thereby to give treatment of the highest order in each locality.

The benefits to the patients were enormous and took away the need to go to a distant Teaching Hospital for proper treatment since this was now available at the local hospital.

In general practice, too, changes were effected and the buying and selling of practices was forbidden. General practitioners were to be paid by the State according to the numbers of patients registered in the practice. These changes marked the foundations of a "New Citadel" of state medicine which was to grow and change over the succeeding decades.

It so happened that while working in King's College Hospital during the London blitz, I came to know John Hunter who was the Senior Surgeon at King's College Hospital but who during the war had become the administrator of Sector 9, one of the sectors into which London had become divided in wartime. He was very friendly with a Dr Patterson who was the newly appointed Senior Administrative Medical Officer of the Newcastle-upon-Tyne Regional Hospital Board.

Dr Patterson felt that there was too much inbreeding of the consultant staff in Newcastle and wished to broaden the inflow of talent into the North East and to staff the new District General Hospitals with fully trained consultants. He had consulted John Hunter who suggested that I may be interested to come to the North East, either to Newcastle or to a new hospital development which was about to take place in Darlington. John Hunter rang me and asked me my views and whether I would be interested in such an appointment.

My first reaction was one of outright refusal as I, like most people in London, envisaged the North East as a land of slag heaps with forests of factory chimneys overhung by a pall of smoke. He pleaded with me to at least visit Darlington and this I agreed to do. As my wife Joan had been in London almost all her life I felt she must come to survey the area in which she might in the future have to live, were I to take this new appointment.

We left Croydon very early on a Saturday morning in May 1950. I was very proud of my new black Ford Anglia priced at £100 and bought without recourse to the huge black market in cars which after the war was then rife throughout the country. Getting through London at an early hour was always easy and we soon reached the old A1 road long before it became a motorway.

The journey north was slow and even slower as we passed through the narrow streets of the elegant town of Stamford and the market place of Grantham long before this town had any association with the Prime Minister of Great Britain. But the main problem was in Doncaster where the combination of a horse-race meeting and a football match with Doncaster Rovers produced a queue of traffic miles long.

It was getting late in the afternoon and fatigue and frustration induced my wife and I to put up at a pub in Darrington. The name Darrington seemed to be an omen for the future as it closely resembled the name of Darlington, one of the objects of my visit.

I was surprised to find Darlington such a nice little town, without smoke and without slag heaps. I had warned Joan that it might be cold in the north and she had taken her fur coat only to find the May weather in Darlington was sweltering. The hospital was an attractive Memorial Hospital which had with its annexes 250 beds.

Impressed with Darlington, I proceeded to Newcastle where there was the second prospective appointment. This was my first visit to Newcastle though I had previously passed through the city on the train on my way to Edinburgh. It was a city of bridges and back streets. On enquiring from a passer-by the way to the Royal Victoria Infirmary, he was most courteous and helpful but neither I nor Joan could understand a single word of the accent of Tyneside and which I was later to know as a Geordie accent.

On our return journey to London we stopped just alongside the city of Durham in one of the only short stretches of dual carriageway which was present on the A1 at that time. I looked down on the great cathedral and the castle and was most impressed by the sight. I was reminded that a former curate at the cathedral had baptised my twin sons at the chapel at King's College Hospital, London. The Reverend Fearnsby was the chaplain at King's during the war and he, John Peel* and Archie Galley† had come to tea at our home in Croydon after the christening. The sight of Durham and this memory of the past gave me a feeling that to settle in the North East would not be impossible.

In the summer of 1950 I attended for interview at the Regional Hospital Board in Newcastle with six other candidates for the appointments at Newcastle and at Darlington. The Newcastle appointment

---

* Sir John Peel, Consultant Gynaecologist, King's College Hospital, Surgeon Gynaecologist to H.M. The Queen.
† Dr A. H. Galley, Consultant Anaesthetist, King's College Hospital.

appeared to be pre-determined and went to the local applicant, as was expected, but the Darlington appointment was a much more open affair.

The chairman of the appointments committee was a Mr Weston-Adamson, who was a remarkable man. Though he suffered from a severe congenital deformity of both arms, he drove his Bentley at speed and flew his own aircraft. He was an excellent chairman and later on we were to become lifelong friends.

On the appointment committee was Professor Bentley, whom I had met in York Military Hospital when we were both in the army, and it was Professor Bentley who had taken the Professorial chair in Surgery from Professor Norman Hodgson at Newcastle. He too was anxious to get new blood into the region and I was encouraged by his attitude. The other medical member was Professor Pybus, a former Professor of Surgery at Newcastle and Dr G. D. Owen who had just been appointed a Senior Consultant Physician to the Friarage Hospital in Northallerton and to the Darlington Memorial Hospital.

Professor Pybus was a miserable, crotchety little man whose only question was to ask me if I had done any research. An answer in the affirmative and a mention of my work on peptic ulcer seemed to satisfy his requirements and I was duly appointed Senior Consultant Surgeon to the Darlington Memorial Hospital and the Friarage Hospital in North-allerton. The acceptance of these appointments was to alter completely my entire professional life.

London before the war was a wonderful place in which to live, and to be sick of London was to be sick of life. Following the ravages of war, repairing and rebuilding started but the city never really gained its pre-war atmosphere. Massive immigration and other restrictions follow-ing the war seemed to have altered the character of the city.

This fact made the thought of leaving London more acceptable, while the challenge of a completely new sphere of activity held out much promise. The practical problem of selling our house in London was overshadowed by the impossibility of buying a house in north Yorkshire or south Durham. Because of this Joan and the family continued to live in our home in South Croydon as we could not vacate the house for fear of its being requisitioned.

I went to live in the Golden Lion Hotel in Northallerton which is a few hundred yards from the Friarage Hospital. This was perhaps fortuitous since it enabled me to organize the start of a Consultant Surgical Service in an area which had never known such a service before.

In former years all major surgery went to Newcastle, Leeds or to London and only the simplest procedures were carried out either in the Memorial Hospital in Darlington or in the Rutson Cottage Hospital in Northallerton where a Mr David Dickson of Middlesborough was the surgeon.

The task that lay ahead was to develop the Friarage Hospital in Northallerton and the Darlington Memorial Hospital as District General Hospitals to provide a standard of treatment that was comparable to that to which I had been accustomed in the Teaching Hospitals in London. It was a task of immense proportions but one which in subsequent years was to give the greatest satisfaction and the reward of a sense of achievement.

13

The District General Hospital

PERHAPS by far the greatest contribution the Health Service has made
to medicine in Britain has been to establish District General Hospitals
throughout the length and breadth of the land. In my new appointment
as Senior Consultant there was, as already mentioned, the task of establishing for the first time in this area a Consultant Surgical Service. The
hospitals in Darlington and Northallerton are mid-way between the
Teaching Centres in Leeds and at Newcastle. In the former years general
practitioners in Darlington had worked hard to provide surgery in this
no-man's-land between the two great centres.

It seemed likely that the hospitals in Darlington and Northallerton
which were different in their origin would be different in their development. The intake of cases to the Friarage Hospital in Northallerton was
from the farming communities of the North Riding of Yorkshire and
from the Yorkshire Dales, while Darlington received cases from the
industrial community in the town, from the small industrial towns in the
southern part of County Durham, and from Teesdale.

THE FRIARAGE HOSPITAL, NORTHALLERTON

The name of this hospital has its roots deep in centuries past, and the
hospital was built in the Friarage Fields the site of a Carmelite Friary
established by Edward III in 1356. The modern hospital started its
existence at the onset of the Second World War.

The Emergency Medical Service (E.M.S.) was instituted to deal with
the medical problem of the war, and new hospitals were established in

many parts of the country. The siting of an E.M.S. hospital in North-allerton was to deal with the casualties resulting from the possible bombing of the heavy industrial plants on Teesside. In the event this situation did not arise and Teesside largely escaped air attack so the hospital was not used for its intended purpose.

The first use of the hospital was for the accommodation of troops returning from the evacuation of Dunkirk, but thereafter assumed its proper function as a hospital in the autumn of 1940. However, because of developments in the war the hospital was taken over by the Royal Air Force in January 1943.

The market town of Northallerton is located in the plain of York which contained a great number of R.A.F. airfields and airstrips. It was from this area and from other eastern counties that our bombers set out to strike at the heart of the German war machine. It is not surprising that an R.A.F. hospital was located in Northallerton during the war to deal with the surgical problems and accidents associated with such a large concentration of service personnel.

After the war there was a suggestion that the R.A.F. hospital should become a Police Training Centre, but Dr Patterson, the Senior Administrative Medical Officer at the Newcastle Regional Hospital Board was determined that it should continue to be a hospital to serve the most southern part of the region. In the event his views prevailed. Dr Patterson was also determined that he would obtain a new generation of consultants to staff not only the Friarage Hospital in Northallerton but also the Memorial Hospital in Darlington.

To achieve his objectives three senior posts covering both hospitals were created, one in medicine, one in gynaecology and obstetrics, and one in surgery. The appointment in gynaecology and obstetrics was filled by Professor J. H. Hovell who had been a professor of obstetrics in the University of Khartoum. The appointment in medicine was filled by Dr G. D. Owen who had been the first assistant to Lord Cohen in Liverpool. I was the last to be appointed having been first assistant to Professor Ian Aird, the Professor of Surgery at the London Postgraduate Medical School at Hammersmith Hospital.

The Friarage Hospital was a Nissen-hutted Emergency Service type of hospital of 300 beds. Two lines of huts were connected by two corridors; on the surgical side the corridor was open but with overhead cover, while on the medical side the corridor was covered in.

Each ward contained 24 beds with 4 side wards and communal facilities. The conditions were similar to those of any Service Hospital. The operating theatres were primitive without air conditioning. The main theatre opened into a hospital corridor on one side and into a steam filled sterilizing room on the other. The nurse staffing of the hospital in general was rudimentary and originally only eleven State Registered Nurses were employed, while the remainder were assistant nurses and student nurses in various stages of training. The spirit and motivation of the nursing staff was first class, and after a year or two the staff was enhanced by the appointment of Miss Cassie Harker who proved to be a most progressive Matron and took over from "Gertie" Inman who was the first matron after she retired from the R.A.F.

In due course the Friarage Hospital rapidly gained a well deserved reputation. The work and problems encountered in these early development days are outlined in an excellent book written by Cassie Harker, *Call Me Matron*.[15] This book portrays the nursing development in both Northallerton and in Darlington and it was to her excellence both as a nurse and as an administrator that the hospital service in this area owes a very great debt of gratitude.

One of the most pleasant features of working at the Friarage Hospital was the attitude of the secretary and his helpers. I remember as soon as I arrived at the hospital the secretary Michael Wallace came to greet me. He told me that if there was anything I wanted, to come to him and he would do all he could to provide me with help and he was as good as his word. This was the beginning of twenty-seven very happy and productive years at the Friarage Hospital.

In Northallerton in addition to the Friarage Hospital there was a small cottage hospital called The Rutson Hospital which was staffed by the local general practitioners. The outstanding personality was Dr D. M. MacKenzie,* who was a major force in both clinical medicine and medical politics. I was given a great welcome at the Rutson Hospital by the

---

* Dr D. M. MacKenzie, O.B.E., general practitioner, Northallerton. Member of the Hospital Management Committee.

Matron, Miss Phillips. Her second in command Sister Frances Green,* combined the work of a ward sister and theatre work with uncanny skill. It was a great pleasure that two of these persons Dr MacKenzie and Sister Green were honoured for their work in medicine and in nursing in the North Riding of Yorkshire.

At the Rutson Hospital one had the opportunity of meeting and consulting with the general practitioners which helped not only in the management of the patients but also in welding the profession into a united body whose voice could be heard.

The Rutson was the Health Centre in Northallerton and its medical voice.

DARLINGTON MEMORIAL HOSPITAL

The tradition of Darlington Memorial Hospital was very different and of longer standing. Details of the earliest hospital developments are excellently described in a recent publication by Sister Joan Young who worked in my Unit.

The old hospital infirmary was replaced by a new hospital which was sited at The Elms in Woodlands Road in Darlington. The first turf was cut by the late Lady Barnard in 1925, and the foundation stone was laid by Lord Daryington (Pike Pease) on 26 July 1926. This hospital was representative of a large number of "Memorial Hospitals" built in the memory of those who died in the First World War.

In this respect the Memorial Hospital was very special in that included in those commemorated in the memorial hall were a famous family of heroes known as "The Bradford Boys" or the "Fighting Bradfords" as already noted. Of four brothers three died in action and all of the four were decorated. Ronald was the youngest brigadier in the British Army and won the Victoria Cross and the Military Cross, George won the Victoria Cross at Zeebrugge and James won the Military Cross. The only surviving brother was Thomas who won the D.S.O. and in later life returned to Darlington and died in his late eighties.

It was with great pride that I showed many surgeons who came to

---

* Sister F. M. Green, M.B.E., Sister in Charge, Rutson Hospital, Northallerton.

FIGURE 9. *General view of Darlington Memorial Hospital showing the original hospital and in the right background the new hospital.*

FIGURE 10. *The porch erected in memory of those killed in both world wars, but with the special mention of Brigadier Ronald Bradford, V.C., M.C. and his heroic brothers, 'The Fighting Bradfords'.*

115

visit me from all over the world the names of these heroes in our Memorial Hall. (Fig. 9 & Fig. 10)

My welcome at this 250 bedded hospital was very different from that at the Friarage Hospital. The hospital secretary at the Memorial Hospital, by a very strange quirk of fate, was a conscientious objector during the war, a fact that may have influenced his attitude and behaviour over many years. As he did not come to meet me, I felt that I should go to see him in his office, and made an appointment.

He was late for our appointment and then kept me waiting while he talked to one of his junior office staff apparently to impress me with his importance. It was obvious that the hospital was run by a series of committees completely under the control of this secretary. As Senior Consultant Surgeon to the hospital I had been allocated in my absence five beds, one out-patient session, and emergency duty one week in five. The hospital was staffed by general practitioner surgeons who had elected to give up general practice and to concentrate on hospital work. It was rather like a large cottage hospital but did have a nurse training school.

The prospects of establishing a first class surgical Consultant Service in Darlington appeared bleak indeed. I expressed my anxieties to Dr Patterson, the Senior Administrative Medical Officer, and was prepared to leave. He persuaded me to stay and appointed Dr Owen and myself on to the Hospital Management Committee where we could influence the thinking of the committee and start the process of bringing the hospital into its new role as a District General Hospital.

Dr Douglas Owen was a sound and sensible clinician who had a deep understanding of people and of medical politics. He was already serving as a member of the Management Committee at Northallerton and was on the committee that appointed me as surgeon.

When the post of Matron became vacant at the Friarage Hospital it was Dr Owen who recommended Cassie Harker as a candidate as he had met her and seen her work in Liverpool when he worked with Lord Cohen. In a very competitive field she was appointed, an event which was indeed most fortunate. She had held many senior posts and she had been theatre sister to Professor Phillip Allison at Leeds General Infirmary. This training not only provided her with an outlook on surgical problems, but also the rigid discipline of the operating theatre could be applied to developing the hospital service. I had the greatest respect for both Douglas Owen and Cassie Harker and the three of us formed a triumvirate that was most progressive, happy and successful. To crown it all, on the retirement of Michael Wallace, the secretary at the Friarage Hospital, a new and young progressive secretary, Alan Wilson, joined the team.

Alan Wilson was, indeed, a charming and most successful man and it was a pleasure to work with him over a period of many years. He had been a pilot in the Royal Air Force and brought to the hospital administration all the traditions of those who have worked in a Service distinct to those who have worked in commerce.

In later years when Cassie Harker decided to apply for the appointment of Matron at Darlington Memorial Hospital, she was successful and the trio were able to continue developments, albeit with many local difficulties, as outlined in Cassie Harker's book.[15]

Assessment of the position and the personalities involved in each hospital led to the conclusion that the Friarage and Darlington Memorial Hospital could best be served by separate development. This hospital "apartheid" allowed of different policies being adopted in each hospital over a wide range of subjects. As time went on a friendly rivalry developed which resulted in advantage to both these institutions. In a clinical sense, too, this was an advantage since different modalities of management and treatment could be compared between the two hospitals.

MANAGEMENT

Each hospital was under the direction of a Management Committee. The members of the committee were drawn from all walks of life and were indeed representative of the local population. The general spirit was well directed to provide for the needs of the people. Though local councillors were included in the membership only rarely did politics intrude into the running of the hospitals.

The local populace felt that they were involved and if any problem arose they knew exactly who to go to to make their complaints or to have their questions answered. On each committee there were representatives of the consultants from the hospitals as well as local general practitioners.

Supporting the Management Committee there were medical and

nursing advisory committees who could express their views on developments or answer problems referred from the main committee. This simple structure worked well for many years and had the confidence of the public and of the professions. The hospital secretary was the administrator and acted as a co-ordinator and a figure head. In each hospital there was one administrator which is very different from today when there are dozens of administrators in Darlington alone.

As often happens, a successful system becomes over-developed and leads to its own destruction on a national scale. The committee structure became too involved and a series of interdigitating bodies were formed which have been outlined in the "cogwheel" reports.[1]

As time went on it was apparent that simple problems were referred to committees and became lost in the system so that decisions were not made and time was wasted. The committee structure became too complex and began to fall into disrepute. There followed a geometric progression of the appointments of administrators and more recently of managers which have contributed to the structure of a new citadel in medical administration and still further changes are now taking place. It is estimated that the bill for management has grown eighteen fold in the last seven years (David Fletcher – Health Service Correspondent, *Daily Telegraph*, 13 January 1994). Contemporaneously, the appointment of managers has further increased the numbers of lay staff at the expense of those who care for the sick.

14

Developing a Consultant Surgical Service

IT IS RARE to have the opportunity of starting a Consultant Surgical Service in any area for the very first time. Most appointments in surgery are merely replacements and their tenure a continuation of the traditions and practices of the past. In Northallerton the position was entirely new, the former R.A.F. hospital had no tradition and the expectations of the patients quite unknown. In Darlington the tradition was that of a general practitioner surgical service. This service had to be made to evolve into the latter half of the twentieth century. This unique situation presented opportunities for clinical studies and research unfettered by previous practice and custom.

THE GENERAL PRACTITIONER

It seemed that the success of this new venture would depend in the first instance on gaining the confidence of the general practitioners and of good relationships between the general practitioner and the hospital consultants. It would also depend, in the second place, on the provision of excellence of patient care in the hospitals.

The introduction of the National Health Service provided a new impetus for development in the hospital service, while the domiciliary consultation scheme under the National Health Service also played an important part. This domiciliary visiting system enabled any patients, even the poorest, to have a consultant see them in their own homes with the general practitioner in attendance. This scheme provided me with my first experience of domiciliary consultation outside London.

My first consultation was to a patient in Wensleydale, an area now internationally known as Herriot Country, after the famous books written by a local veterinary surgeon (James White).

The call came to the Friarage Hospital on Friday afternoon just after the completion of an operating session. Unfamiliar with the district I armed myself with a map and set out from Northallerton on the road to Bedale, the gateway to Wensleydale. On the way I caught sight of the Vale of York stretching to the west as far as the Pennine Hills. Crossing over a typical type of Yorkshire bridge at Morton-on-Swale and crossing the old Great North Road at Leeming Bar I arrived at the market town of Bedale.

It was a striking little town with its cobbled market place, its ancient cross in the middle of the town and the tower of the Parish Church acting like a sentinel as the road passed on its way into Wensleydale.

Never having visited the Dales before I found the winding roads enchanting, and the scenery constantly changing as I got further up the dale on the way to Aysgarth. The hedgerows of the lower dale gave place to the dry-stone wall boundaries with the odd looking ridge of stones sticking out in rows from the side of the wall. I thought that these protruding stones were there to enable people to climb over the wall, but I was soon to learn that they were cross members to enhance the strength of the dry wall. The hills on either side of the road got higher and higher and the dale narrowed as the fields of grass became replaced by moorland.

The village of Aysgarth, where I was to consult with Dr William Pickles, was reached just before teatime and he was due to join me soon.

Dr Pickles had attained a national and international reputation for his work on epidemiology and infective diseases. He, by careful note-keeping and map locations, had proved that what was formerly known as catarrhal jaundice, was in fact an infective disease characterised by a very long incubation period and now known as infective hepatitis.

I was most interested to meet this country doctor who had been awarded many honours and who had accepted invitations to lecture all over the world. He was almost a mythological figure who had written a book, *Epidemiology in General Practice*, which though very small had become a classic.[16]

120

Dr Pickles came from a family of doctors and of his six brothers all but one had qualified in medicine. He had been a dresser to Lord Moynihan the famous surgeon of Leeds soon after qualifying but strangely enough did not begin his work in general practice on infective diseases until he was well over forty. It was as the result of his special interest in epidemiology that his book was published.

At Aysgarth I was met by his partners, Drs. Bernard and Kitty Coltman, who had joined his practice just after the war. We sat down in their lounge and viewed the glories of the dales which to me was a new and wonderful experience. We talked of London where I had trained and of Leeds where the Coltmans qualified. In that most relaxed atmosphere I began for the first time to absorb the culture of the Yorkshire Dales.

After about half an hour Dr Pickles made his entry. He was a big, thick-set man with greying hair and penetrating eyes. He looked me up and down and after an interval that seemed almost as long as the incubation period of infective hepatitis, he made a decision that I was a suitable consultant to see his patient. This decision was greeted by the announcement that it was time for tea.

Tea was a very prolonged affair and he talked much of Yorkshire life, of its customs and culture and of its climate. Finally the time had come to go to see the patient.

The Coltmans got into the front seats of an open convertible Hillman Minx while Pickles and I got into the back. The journey along the narrow dales road was a conducted tour with Pickles as the guide and courier. He remarked on every detail of the countryside and indeed of its inhabitants, all of whom were his patients and he had in fact delivered most of them. As we passed a little group of trees on the hill-side he said to me, "Do you see yonder spinney? That's where the headless horseman rides."

I was most amused and burst out laughing only to find that he became suddenly very silent. I was at loss to know why I had caused such offence as he seemed to be deeply upset. I was to learn the reason some years later when one of my registrars, a Doctor Forsyth, did a locum in the Pickles practice. I discovered from Dr Forsyth that Dr Pickles maintained that he himself had seen the headless horseman. The fact that I had laughed at his observations had been to doubt his veracity, and the accuracy of his observations.

Thereafter we travelled in silence down the dale until we reached a sign-post pointing to the village of West Burton. The side road was even narrower and more winding as we approached the charming little village.

The main road in the village was flanked on either side with well mown village lawns and there were pavements just in front of the rows of cottages to either side. We ascended the slight rise leading to the upper end of the village green and then turned left to reach the front of a typical Yorkshire cottage. There was no sign of any people in the village nor of any activity as the Hillman pulled to a halt outside the front door.

Pickles announced that this was the house and promptly led the way to the door which was ajar in anticipation of our arrival. He walked straight into the living room and introduced me as the new Consultant Surgeon from London, who had come to work at the Friarage Hospital in Northallerton.

The living room was well filled with silent relatives who gave a Yorkshire nod of recognition while the patient's wife ascended the open staircase that led from the living room to the bedroom. I could feel that every eye was watching every step that we took, and the squeaking of the dry boards of the stairway was welcome in that it broke the ominous silence.

There in the little bedroom was an elderly man lying on a neatly made bed. He lay quietly with his hands crossed over what seemed like a rather protuberant abdomen.

On the floor to the side of the bed there was a jug and basin, the washing equipment of any Victorian home. From under the counterpane a red rubber tube emerged and wound its serpiginous course across the floor to ascend over the edge of the basin and to reach and enter into the jug contained in the basin. It was obvious that this apparatus was concerned with the urinary system and that when the jug was full of urine the basin acted as an overflow receptacle.

I took the patient's clinical history and it was apparent that he had developed an acute urinary obstruction many years ago and to enable him to pass water a tube had been inserted through the abdomen into the bladder to deal with the problem.

The tube had been there, astonishingly, for some seventeen years and the patient wondered if, as a new London-trained surgeon, I could do anything to remove the tube and to allow him to pass his urine in the normal way.

The surgical problem itself was easy and I explained to him that his prostate gland was enlarged and if the gland was removed he could return to living a normal life like any other man. He appeared pleased with this opinion which held out the prospect of getting rid of the tube, but I thought I could detect that he was perhaps a little sceptical and indeed apprehensive about the result of the operation.

After much Yorkshire discussion he decided to have the operation. With this decision his wife was in full agreement and to quote her exact words she found there were 'very intimate occasions when the tube got in the way', and she too would welcome its removal. I felt that at this stage all had now been agreed and that there was nothing more to be said, but in this I was very much mistaken.

On descending the stairs every face looked up from the living-room and I could feel as well as see that every eye was on me. When we had both reached the living-room, the patient's son, a ruddy faced dales farmer, looked me straight in the eye and said, "What's to do?".

I explained once again to this little assembly what the proposal was and what the prospects were likely to be. Suddenly there was much discussion between the various relatives and arrangements were made between the various members of the family. I had the strong feeling that a funereal wake was being planned rather than an admission to hospital.

At the same time the quiet village became suddenly active and those who had been secretly observing the visit emerged from behind the curtains fully to participate in the great event. The patient thereafter was taken from his home by ambulance in an atmosphere as though this were his last journey and from which he would never return. In due course the operation, as anticipated, turned out to be a second stage prostatectomy and after operation he returned home 2–3 weeks later much to the consternation of the entire village.

It is difficult to know what ceremony can follow a funeral wake. The effect of treatment on this single patient was revealing and dramatic. Patients from all over the dales came, holding their supra-pubic tubes, to the hospital to see if they too could have this marvellous "new operation".

It was all too obvious what was required and it took a year or two to work through the backlog of operations for such cases of enlarged prostate.

It was from domiciliary visits that much was learned about the medical services in the area, the expectations of the patients, and the northern way of life. I remember seeing a young boy, the son of a famous race-horse trainer, who developed with typical suddenness an acute obstructive appendicitis. Even knowing the risk of sudden perforation his father was considering taking his son to London for emergency operation at this time, because there was little faith in the local surgical skills. He was in fact admitted to the Friarage Hospital, Northallerton and after appendicectomy made a very easy recovery.

The success of this apparently normal procedure produced a great feeling of confidence in the close knit horse racing fraternity in the north.

Similarly, a famous race-horse owner perforated his duodenal ulcer while driving his Bentley car past the Catterick race-course. He, too, was dealt with at the hospital in Northallerton, which again made this particular fraternity realize that in the newly established District General Hospital surgical treatment could match that obtained in London or at other Teaching Hospitals. This particular patient related that in former years he had developed acute appendicitis and was seen by a famous Teaching Hospital Surgeon who came down from Newcastle to see him in his home.

At consultation, operation was advised and the surgeon returned to Newcastle to get his instruments to perform the operation. The patient recounted with some amusement that he had two bills, one for the clinical visit and one for going back to Newcastle to fetch the necessary surgical instruments.

A very pleasant feature of domiciliary visits in the North Riding of Yorkshire was that the general practitioner virtually always attended at the consultation. On one occasion I had a request to call for the general practitioner at his surgery and then go together to the patient's house which was somewhat difficult to find. The call came from "young" Dr Williams of Richmond.

Accordingly, I went to this lovely Yorkshire town, with its medieval castle which in years gone by guarded Swaledale against the invading Scots, and located his surgery in one of the ancient streets of the town. As I pulled up outside the surgery a very elderly doctor tottered down the steps to greet me, he was "young" Dr Williams. Apparently the doctor had joined his father in the practice and in consequence he was known as "young" Dr Williams and he had indeed retained this title until he died in old age.

In Darlington the general practitioners were less often present in domiciliary consultations, and this reflected the higher pressure of clinical work in the towns as distinct from the country areas.

There was no doubt that both in Darlington and in the surrounding country the standard of general practice was very much higher than that which I had observed when working in London. The constant meetings with the general practitioners at patients' homes or at the Cottage Hospitals in Northallerton (Rutson), Barnard Castle (Richardson), or at Richmond (Victoria) blended the whole of the medical services together. The general practitioner service, now graced by the term Primary Health Care Team, and the Consultant Hospital Service could merge into a continuity of service which was indeed commendable.

It is rather disturbing that the present tendency is to separate these two aspects of clinical care, and this segmentation has become a feature of the new "Citadel" in medicine, where the general practitioner and the consultant no longer have the mutual respect and confidence of former years.

THE HOSPITALS

The other essential elements in developing a surgical service was to attain a high standard of work and patient care in the hospital. Like Caesar's Gaul, the hospital service is divided into three parts; the Out-Patient Clinic which is comparable to the shop window of commerce, the Ward which is where the caring aspects of surgery can have their fulfilment, and the Operating Theatre where the survival and future of the patient is largely determined.

(A) OUT-PATIENT CLINICS

Out-Patient Clinics were established in the Memorial Hospital in Darlington and at the Friarage and Rutson Hospitals in Northallerton.

Experience in London Hospitals had shown that patients had often to wait many anxious hours before being seen by the surgeon in the clinic. To mitigate this problem in the new developing service the clinics were divided into segments, and block bookings in periods of half an hour were established, which was a great improvement on the former system. Though this arrangement was not ideal, it was preferable to giving individual appointment times to every patient which would be a very expensive waste of consultant time and would diminish very greatly the total number of patients seen.

It is interesting to note that the introduction of a Patients Charter is now being attempted and one of its objectives is to eliminate the waiting time in the Out-Patient Department by giving a fixed appointment time. It is quite apparent that any attempt at an individual appointment system will greatly limit the total work load. It will also result in some patients absorbing time that their case does not merit, while at the same time patients requiring more time will have their consultation abbreviated to meet the time schedule which has been laid down in the Patients Charter.

This system, outlined in the charter, if implemented would reduce the total number of patients seen in the Out-Patients Clinic by seventy-five per cent, and this would result in much hardship to a greater number of people.

The concept of the Patients Charter, though laudable in many ways in its political intent, would diminish the ability of the hospital service to cope with an ever increasing work load, and would result in greater rather than less hardship for those with serious disease.

One of the most time absorbing features of medical practice is the writing of patients notes in long hand. This slow process diverts the clinicians attention from patient observation, and with pressure of work and short-age of time, notes are often abbreviated, incomplete and illegible. During the war, and especially during the heavy casualty intake from the Second Front, I was, as already mentioned, in charge of a mobile surgical unit. The unit consisted of a surgeon in charge, an anaesthetist, a surgical assistant, a theatre sister and a "scribe". The job of the scribe was to take notes and to look after documentation and constantly to attend on the surgical team. Experience showed the immense value of the "scribe" as a member of the whole team. As time went on the concept of the scribe grew in importance in my mind and I decided that as soon as I was in charge of a civilian unit this principle would be extended.

In modern terms the "scribe" is now the medical secretary and her role is now even more important than before.

The medical secretary produces notes that are full, neat and easily readable. This is of immense value to the clinician, the research worker and the hospital administration. Eliminating the slow process of writing notes greatly increases the number of patients seen and eliminates the time wasted in trying to read illegible notes, especially in the District General Hospitals where there are no undergraduate students to take and write up case histories.

To obtain a personal medical secretary is indeed a long and arduous struggle.

As every consultant knows, since the introduction of the Health Service, there has been a quite staggering increase in administration. The administrators seem to have no difficulty in getting secretaries and the pay scale and grading of these secretaries is far above the secretary who has to do the medical work.

However, persistent pressure over a period of several years enabled me to have a personal secretary who really became a personal assistant and made a major contribution to the development of the Surgical Unit.

After two part-time secretaries I had the good fortunate to obtain the full time services of a secretary who, having spent ten years in industry, had a great desire to enter the medical field.

Eileen Raine started in my unit in 1962 at a time when the clinical load was very heavy. Her advent heralded a new era of efficiency which was to last for over fifteen years. She attended every clinic and became highly skilled in abstracting the clinical history and typing the reports to the general practitioners on the same day on which the patient was seen. (Fig. 11)

This was of immense value to the consultant, the patient, and the general practitioner. This contrasts markedly with the situation often experienced today when long delays in getting reports to general practitioners seems to be commonplace and results in time-wasting telephone calls to the hospital to get vital information about the patient.

In addition my secretary attended the Grand Ward Round and this provided a continuity of medical secretarial supervision and resulted in

FIGURE 11. *Surgical Out-patient Clinic. The author with two trainee surgeons, Sister Fairpo, his medical secretary Eileen Raine taking notes, and Sister Dellbridge and her Staff Nurse in attendance. The X-ray on the viewing box shows a cancer of the gullet.*

the ward notes being of an equally high standard to those in the Out-Patient Department.

When completely new techniques were being evolved in operations for cancer of the oesophagus, she came to the operating theatre so that every detail of the operating technique was recorded at the time of the operation. This laid the foundation for the accurate details that were involved in the large number of publications in textbooks and in surgical journals which were made on the diagnosis and operative treatment of oesophageal cancer, and also in the surgical treatment of peptic ulcer.

It is with great pleasure that I record my thanks to Eileen, not only in these clinical duties, but also for her help in arranging for the visits of individual surgeons from all over the world, and of surgical clubs from England, Ireland and Spain.

Of very special interest was the visit from the President and Council of the Royal College of Surgeons of England. The Royal College elects, each year, Hunterian Professors who give a lecture at the Royal College in London. These lectures date back to 1805, and commemorate John Hunter who was, perhaps, the most famous of all surgeons. On this occasion the President agreed that my Hunterian Lecture could be given at Darlington Memorial Hospital and this was the first Hunterian Lecture ever to be held outside London in a District General Hospital. This was an entirely new departure and required a great deal of organization. Eileen organized this function with great efficiency and details of this very special occasion are recorded in Chapter 20.

In many respects the medical secretary made a contribution to the surgical unit equivalent to that of the ward sister or that of the theatre sister. It is a measure of administrative lack of insight that even today the importance of the medical secretary has not been appreciated.

In the organization of the Out-Patient clinic it is important to use a central consulting room for interview, flanked on either side by examination rooms, as this allows the history of one patient to be taken while another patient is getting undressed ready for examination. This simple arrangement saves a great deal of time and greatly increases the number of patients being seen. It is disappointing to see new hospital Out-Patient departments designed without provision for this efficient and simple arrangement.

THE HOSPITAL WARD

It is in the hospital ward that the patient first experiences medical care. It is here the nursing skills and the medical knowledge combine in the treatment of disease. Before the introduction of the National Health Service there was a very close partnership between the nursing and the medical professions which was much to their mutual benefit. Regrettably in recent years the move to nursing independence has been in vogue and has resulted in much absurdity.

In what is essentially a practical "hands on" profession there has emerged the "consultant" nurse whose function is to advise the nurses on the very procedures which they should be carrying out themselves. This system is in operation in Canada and the United States of America and from my observations, the "graduate" nurse is neither a good nurse nor a properly trained doctor.

129

During the visits I made to hospitals in Canada and the U.S.A., surgeons that I met were full of praise for the British nurse, and only wished that they were more available in North America. They often said "if only we could have British nurses". It is a strange paradox that while North America is crying out for British nurses, the leaders of the Nursing profession in Britain should be changing to the American system, while the American surgeons want the British nurse.

The importance of ward work was fully realized and a close partnership between the nursing and the medical staff has been the underlying theme in my District General Hospitals. The Grand Ward Round considered each patient's problem with the whole medical staff and with the consultant radiologist in attendance. The effect on the confidence of the patient was quite apparent for they knew that their case had been considered and discussed and appropriate management would be implemented.

The value of experienced and dedicated ward sisters is essential to obtain a high standard of care. In the London Teaching hospitals the ward sister knew the treatment routines and few problems arose.

However, in the new district hospitals, where for the first time consultant services were established and very major surgery performed, the position was very different. In this instance it was felt that, for guidance and help in the treatment regimes, that these should be outlined for the use of both the resident medical and the nursing staff. These instructions resembled the standing orders which I encountered during army service.

Specific duties and routines were therefore known by all concerned in patient care and prevented the sequence, "Order – Counter Order – Disorder".

Over the years the Ward Book of treatment regimes evolved in the Friarage Hospital in Northallerton and in the Memorial Hospital in Darlington. It was entitled "Suggestions for Surgical Management" and came to be regarded as a "Surgical Bible". On one occasion a member of the British and Foreign Bible Society visited one of the wards and asked whether there was a Bible on the ward. The ward sister responded immediately and said that there was and promptly produced the "Surgical Bible"!

One great advantage of a written book of guidance is that it prevented an experienced ward sister from intimidating a newly qualified house surgeon and undermining the morale of the more junior members of the medical staff.

At this time the intensive care unit had not come into operation and all cases however serious were treated in the surgical wards. The very ill were located nearest to the nurses station so that they had maximum supervision, while those patients who had become convalescent were moved progressively out of the area of high dependency.

Though appreciating the advantages of the intensive care unit in medical treatment, there is the disadvantage that the staff working in this type of unit only deal with those that are very ill and they are deprived of the satisfaction of seeing patients admitted seriously ill and then progress to full recovery. It is a great tribute to the nursing staff that they were able to manage the very major surgery in the general ward and to produce mortality rates that were quite the envy of many surgical centres.

I would like to pay tribute to my Ward Sisters for their excellent work, especially Sister Dicks and Sister Foster at Darlington Memorial Hospital, to Sister Plows and Sister Thompson and Sister Hinks at the Friarage Hospital and to Sister Green at the Rutson Hospital in Northallerton.

THE OPERATING THEATRE

In former years the great importance of the operating theatre was not fully appreciated in many hospitals. The fact that in the North East some distinguished surgeons were able to perform operations in the patient's home (which was a situation referred to as "kitchen table surgery") demeaned the vital role of the operating theatre in contributing to surgical success.

Though in Darlington Memorial Hospital there was a theatre superintendent there were at first no theatre teams and in cases of shortage of staff, any nurse from any department was drafted in to make up for the shortage. In addition there were constant changes of staff under the misguided excuse of "training" and this prevented the development of excellent theatre technique.

In the first major thoraco-abdominal operation carried out in the

Darlington Memorial Hospital for cancer of the stomach (where the chest cavity and the abdomen were opened up), unknown to me the staff were changed in the middle of the procedure. As the result of this, at the end of the operation, the nurses who remained on duty could not account for all the swabs that had been used and some swabs were apparently missing. I insisted that all nurses who had taken part in the operation should be recalled.

Pandemonium broke out as the town of Darlington and the surrounding district was scoured to contact and bring back the nurses who had gone off duty in the middle of the operation.

What had happened was that the swab counts had been handed over from one nurse to another as each nurse had gone off duty and this swap over had occurred on many occasions within this single operation. After much searching in homes and pubs, in cinemas and in dance halls, all missing nurses were located and brought back into the operating theatre. As all the swabs were laid out on the operating theatre floor and recounted it was found that far from two swabs being missing, there were four too many.

Swab counts are a matter of mathematical recording and should not rely on the memory of nurses or on the long tape leashes attached to the swabs. Memory can play tricks, and leashes attached to abdominal packs can be cut in the course and tension of a long and difficult case as had happened in this very instance.

Having assured myself that there were no swabs remaining either in the chest cavity or in the abdomen of the patient, I closed the wound and went straight to the matron's office.

I was greeted with all the excuses about difficulties with staff and staff training and a thousand reasons why a proper operating team could not be formed. With persistent obstruction it seemed unlikely that the essential changes that were necessary could be obtained from the then nursing administrative staff. I decided on another approach and that I would invoke the help of the Management Committee of whom I had just become a member.

Each month, on Wednesday afternoon, the Management Committee at Darlington met in the elegant board room overlooked by portraits of former chairmen. The chairman at this time was an Alderman Best who was a local man with reasonable left-wing tendencies. His supporting members were drawn from all walks of life and from all moderate political opinions.

At the meeting it was customary for the hospital secretary to sit on the chairman's right whispering to him only the information that he wished the chairman to know, which indeed was not necessarily all the information that he ought to know.

The item of theatre staffing was put at the bottom of the agenda and when at last the item was reached it was time for tea and all the members were a little fatigued. George Beckwith, the secretary, mentioned that the new surgeon wished to discuss theatre staffing but that he and the matron had already dealt with the matter. However my colleague, Dr Douglas Owen, with typical political insight, suggested that the committee might like to know direct from me what my views were.

While sipping his tea and whispering to George, the chairman reluctantly agreed that I should give my views.

As I had come from the operating theatre to the management committee fresh from the scene where one week previously I had had my first experience of doing major surgery at the Darlington Memorial Hospital, the memories of this occasion were fresh in my mind and I described to the committee the scene of the previous week.

I told them of the missing swabs and of the changing nurses. Of sending the police to the nurses' homes, of ringing the local Odeon cinema to try to locate the missing nursing staff, who were the only people who could give details of the vital swab count. On hearing this the tea party stopped and every member became silent.

At this point I drew a simile to describe the operating theatre situation and to inject reality and urgency into my problem.

Imagine, I said, that you were flying across the Atlantic and in mid flight the pilot announces on the intercom that he never had flown the aircraft before but he was in fact a trained pilot. Ten minutes later the flight engineer announces that he has had no experience with turbo-prop engines but again assured you that he was a trained engineer. A final message from the navigator states that he had always navigated on the polar route and that he was now navigating this particular route for the first time, but that he had been trained.

By this time some of the committee looked quite pale and anxious as beads of perspiration appeared on their faces on visualizing such a scenario. I explained that a comparable situation was arising every day in their own operating theatre, here in Darlington. I got my way without further discussion.

A theatre operating team must be a group who have been trained and who work together, without changes in the key staff, as in training an air crew. My recommendation was that a theatre sister, a "permanent" staff nurse, and a staff nurse on annual contract should work together with two probationary nurse, who were on rotation.

To each team there must be attached a theatre technician who helps in the lifting of patients, the positioning of patients on the operating table, and adjusting the theatre operating light.

I regarded the technician as a vital part of the team and the appointment attracted many ex-service men.* The system was put into operation in both my hospitals and was a very great success. It was commented on with enthusiasm over many years when visiting surgeons from all over the world came to see the operating theatres at work.

I have always believed that surgical technique is of vital importance and that each manoeuvre should be carried out with precision and minimum of movement. That the vascular pedicles should be secured at the outset of a procedure and that identification of and respect for tissue planes leads to "bloodless" surgery. This obviates the eternal dabbing with swabs which damages the tissue, obscures the operative field, produces increased blood and fluid loss and contributes to surgical shock.

If a technique is well thought out and adhered to on every occasion the theatre sister and the team follow the technique and the sister can place the right instrument into the surgeon's hand at just the right time. This obviates the distraction of asking for instruments. Other than a few hand gestures and signals, no words need be spoken at even the most complex operation.

I was always very impressed with the R.A.F. Regiment Drill Squad who could perform complex drill procedures for fifteen minutes without a single command. If these servicemen can acquire that precision why not a surgical team?

---

* Sgt Arthur Wilde—ex Scots Guard

The operating theatre is perhaps the most work intensive area in any surgical unit. The use of proper operating teams is essential to obtain the highest standards of work and the greatest throughput of patients.

Time and action studies were carried out and it was quite apparent that formerly there were frequent delays in the interval between operating on one patient and awaiting the next. This produced frustration to the staff and upset the whole rhythm of theatre work.

The use of a two-theatre technique with two teams and two anaesthetists avoided this problem. With a proper mix of general surgical cases, the surgeon can move from one theatre to another and while the surgical registrar is sewing up the wound, the next case can be started. In this way very large operating lists can be completed without frustration and without fatigue.

A single major time-consuming case should be operated on at a time when only a single theatre was available so that there was no obstruction to the flow of theatre cases.

Theatre work, therefore, became a central pillar in the development of the surgical service. Recruitment of nurses and technicians was no problem as theatre staff were regarded as an élite, and there was keen competition to be a member of the theatre team.

In later years when individual visitors or surgical groups came to Darlington and Northallerton quite enormous lists could be undertaken and a wide variety of surgical techniques demonstrated. These operating sessions were a great delight to all concerned and it is with pleasure that I acknowledge the theatre sisters* who performed with a distinction which was constantly remarked on by surgeons from all over the world who came especially to Darlington and Northallerton to study surgical technique.

I would like to pay the highest tribute to my theatre sisters at the hospitals who were quite star performers.

The development of a Consultant Surgical Service in Darlington and Northallerton after the inception of the National Health Service provided

---

* Sister Hilary Atkinson, Mrs. Soulsby (nee Wilkinson), Sister McDermid; *Darlington Memorial Hospital.*
Sister Pearson, Sister Ward (nee Potts), Sister Lowe; *Friarage Hospital.*
Sister Green; *Rutson Hospital.*

a standard of patient care of a very high order. In many cases it equalled and even surpassed that obtainable in the large cities of Britain.

This is a state of affairs which is repeated all over this country and if the District General Hospitals get the right support there should be no need whatever in the present day for general practitioners who hold their own budgets to shop around looking for cut price surgery in another district. The fixing of a contract with one particular hospital or one particular surgeon, far from increasing choice, tends to limit the choice.

I have always regarded the consultants' function as serving but not being the servant of the general practitioners. The general practitioners then had a freedom of choice in selecting the most suitable consultant appropriate to the patients' needs. Today the most recent development in the National Health Service has resulted in budget-holding practitioners contracting with certain consultants or hospitals for the treatment of a variety of diseases, and far from increasing choice, choice has been restricted and even the patient's wishes curtailed.

15

The Tasks Ahead

WITH the two district hospitals firmly established the road was clear to proceed with clinical work in the Darlington and Northallerton areas, where the need was great and the potential volume of work enormous. With the development of the Consultant Surgical Service there was no longer any need for patients to go to a distant teaching hospital for treatment, and the leak of cases going to London was soon sealed. In orthopaedics too the position was very satisfactory. There were four orthopaedic surgeons at the Friarage Hospital * and it was at this hospital that the major work in this specialty developed with Gilbert Parker playing an important role.

CLINICAL PROBLEMS

It was quite apparent that here in this area in the North there was a "virgin" clinical area where medical research projects could be easily established alongside the routine surgical work. The static communities allowed a more personal approach to the patient and follow up was easy as most people were settled and seldom changed their address. The high standard of general practice and the post war enthusiasm of the hospital staff provided an ideal and indeed an unrepeatable opportunity for real clinical research.

---

* Edward Knowles, F.R.C.S., Gilbert Parker, F.R.C.S.E., Bruno Isserlin, F.R.C.S.E., Edgar Waters, F.R.C.S.E.

I thought of various research projects and considered that dyspepsia was the first and the most important area for further investigations.

In the inter-war years peptic ulcer (duodenal and gastric ulcer) presented a very major problem affecting young and middle aged adults. At the onset of the Second World War the problem became even more acute not only because of recruitment of young people into the armed forces, but also because of a great increase in episodes of perforated ulcer and of bleeding ulcers that occurred in the first two years of the war. In London this was attributed to the strain and stress induced by air attacks and it was felt that nervous strain played a major part in the incidence of ulcer and of its complications.

While a surgeon in the Emergency Medical Service at King's College Hospital I did some experimental work on gastric acidity since excess of acid was thought to be a major factor in the development of peptic ulcer and strain was thought to cause increase in acidity because of nervous influences. I found that on obtaining samples of gastric juice from patients there was a wide variation in the acidity and the volume of gastric secretion.

It was noticed that if samples were obtained during the period of anxiety in an air raid alert the volume and acidity of the gastric juice was high, but under the acute fear of heavy bombardment the acidity and volume of gastric juice fell dramatically. It was quite evident that this confirmed that nervous factors were indeed playing a part in the control of gastric secretion.

It is of special interest that nervous factors could also affect other bodily function. It was quite a common experience for mothers who were breast feeding their infants to realize that during an air raid secretion was sparse or absent while after the "all clear", secretion of milk was copious and the infants' needs more than satisfied.

While doing the work of Harold Edwards in his Gastric Clinic at King's College Hospital I continued this very special interest in peptic ulcer, its cause and its surgical treatment.

Following the teaching of Harold Edwards and the London School of Surgery I considered that the operation of removal of part of the stomach (partial gastrectomy) was preferable to the short circuit operation (gastro-enterostomy) which had been so strongly recommended in the two decades before the Second World War, especially by Lord Moynihan and the Leeds School of Surgery.

At this time, too, as the result of former experience, I had thought that stress and strain were major factors in the cause of ulcer. It seemed appropriate therefore that this subject should be the first research project in this new and special clinical opportunity where the quiet country atmosphere was so different from the pace and stress of London life.

The findings of this project, which continued for twenty-seven years, have already been widely published.[17, 18] It was surprising to find that in the quiet country areas and in the Yorkshire Dales where the pace of life is slow and apparently untroubled, that peptic ulcer should be so prevalent. This seemed to contradict the concepts of the importance of stress and strain gained in the London scene. It may well be that "Herriot Country" produces some other types of strain factors as yet unrecognized.

In the surgical treatment of ulcer the operation of partial removal of the stomach (partial gastrectomy) was put to the test. One thousand cases of peptic ulcer were operated on in the first few years of the study and thereafter their progress was followed up for over twenty-five years.[17, 18]

It became apparent that in expert hands this operation appeared to be superior to the operation of the cutting of the nerves to the stomach (vagotomy) which has been in vogue for the past quarter of a century. This view has been supported very recently in a personal letter from Lloyd Nyhus of Chicago, who is a world authority in this field.*

Fortunately the discovery of new drugs such as Tagamet, Zantac and Losec have been so effective in controlling gastric over secretion that operation is now seldom required for peptic ulcer.

With the development of gastric surgery in the Northallerton and Darlington area a new situation arose in which cases began to come in from other parts of the country and even from London.

There was one famous ulcer case which was referred from a London hospital with persistent severe indigestion even after operation had been

---

* Lloyd M Nyhus, M.D., F.A.C.S. Warren Cole Professor, University of Illinois at Chicago

carried out for dividing the nerves to the stomach, the operation called vagotomy.

In this particular case only the nerves were cut and the stomach itself was not opened at any time. After this operation the patient had many months and years of upper abdominal pain which had been re-investigated many times and the only finding was a persistently distended stomach. This condition was put down to the fact that the patient had had the nerves to his stomach divided (vagotomy), and the denervated stomach had become distended, but had not had what is known as a drainage operation, where the outlet of the stomach is increased in size or a new outlet provided.

Armed with all the X-rays and the results of the investigations carried out in London I explored this patient's abdomen. The stomach was indeed grossly distended and contained a great soft mass. When the stomach was resected and the contents examined it was found that the great mass consisted of what is known as a bezoar or hair ball.

When this bezoar was further examined there was found in the central nucleus of the mass, an abdominal pack with the name of the hospital still discernible. After the stomach was resected (partial gastrectomy) recovery of the patient was excellent and he was so grateful he gave money to help my clinical research.

The technical interest of this case was that a pack left accidentally in the cavity of the abdomen, had through the years ulcerated through the wall of the stomach and entered the stomach cavity where it formed the nucleus of the bezoar or hair ball. This is only one of a wide variety of gastric cases that came to Darlington for gastric surgery.

The second research project was in regard to cancer of the gullet. This type of cancer was a condition which formerly was considered inoperable and indeed incurable. Attempts at operation in the first half of the century had been characterised by dismal failure.

It was, however, in Newcastle-upon-Tyne where the first real indication of future success was to be discovered by Professor Grey Turner in the Royal Victoria Infirmary. In 1933 he was able to remove the gullet from the chest cavity of an old miner who was suffering from cancer of the gullet. Over a period of almost a year he was able to reconstruct a new passage in front of the patient's breast bone so that the patient was able to swallow once again.

On leaving Newcastle-upon-Tyne, Professor Grey Turner was appointed as the first Professor of Surgery at the Postgraduate Medical School at Hammersmith Hospital in London. I had the privilege of meeting Grey Turner at this hospital on several occasions and had talks with him on surgical subjects including those of cancer of the gullet.

Though his series of cases was small and the operative mortality was very high, he was perhaps one of the first surgeons in Britain to point the way to possible future success.

Inspired by his operative enthusiasm I embarked on the operative treatment for cancer of the oesophagus and did the first operations in the Friarage Hospital in Northallerton.

At the start I only attempted operation for growths at the lower end of the gullet just where the gullet enters the stomach. The operative treatment of growths at this site was easier than those at a higher level, and I felt that I should embark on the less complex cases so that the operative risk would be lower and the confidence of the general practitioners and of the patients could be built up. I realized that Grey Turner had much opposition in Newcastle because of the very high mortality of this operation and I was anxious to avoid similar problems arising in this new area in north Yorkshire and in south Durham.

Operations of this type require a complex type of procedure in which the abdomen and the chest cavity are opened to gain access to the growth. Normally, operating in the chest cavity was regarded as the prerogative of the thoracic surgeon but during the war I was constantly dealing with gunshot wounds of the chest and therefore felt that this was well within the sphere of the experienced general surgeon.

It is interesting to note that most of the advances in the operative treatment of cancer of the gullet have come from general surgeons rather than by those surgeons who specialise purely in thoracic (chest) work.

It is true to say that there were those in the Teaching Hospital in Newcastle who viewed my work with disapproval and when I tried to get an image intensifier to assist me in the radiological (X-ray) aspects of the work my application was turned down. However, I was not discouraged with this setback and the great thrill of satisfaction of being able to remove a growth from a gullet and to enable the patient again to eat a normal meal was indeed most encouraging.

At this time I was helped by two general practitioner anaesthetists, Dr J. O. M. Wedderburn* and Dr Kenneth Oldfield.† Their work was excellent and they were prepared to give great time and thought to these special cases.

After ten years of work, growths at the higher and more difficult levels were included in the study and a whole series of new techniques of operation was evolved to deal with growths at every site.[19] A two-phase operation was used for middle-third growths, which was a great advance.

In this procedure the stomach was mobilized through an opening in the abdomen, while the growth was removed by a separate opening in the right side of the chest.

Working in the isolation of a District General Hospital in the northeast of England, I was unaware that Ivor Lewis of the Central Middlesex Hospital and Norman Tanner at St. James's Hospital, Balham, had already begun using this technique now well known as the Lewis-Tanner operation. Even though the Lewis-Tanner operation was a major advance, problems still arose from very high growths and re-joining the gut was difficult and dangerous deep in the chest cavity.

By a strange coincidence at this time I had to go into hospital for an operation and in the quiet peace of convalescence I was considering the problems of gullet removal (oesophagectomy) for high growths and decided that this residual problem could be solved by adding a third cervical phase to the two-phase operation. This would bring the stomach up into the neck where it could be joined easily to the gullet and this would avoid the dangers of joining the gut deep in the chest cavity.

To consider whether this procedure was possible required further investigations to confirm that the stomach would be long enough to reach into the neck and that the blood supply would be adequate to keep the transposed stomach alive.

With the aid of my theatre sister tests were carried out in the post-mortem room of the hospital and as the result of these investigations it

---

* Dr J. O. M. Wedderburn, G.P., Northallerton
† Dr K. H. Oldfield, F.F.A., G.P. Knayton

seemed certain that the technique of bringing the stomach up into the neck would work.

Accordingly, in 1962, the first case of cancer of the middle third of the oesophagus was submitted to the new three-phase procedure. The first stage was an abdominal operation, the next a chest (upper thoracic) procedure and the final stage was carried out in the neck.

As each stage was a very major operation in its own right and had its own special set of instruments and ligatures, an interval was allowed between each stage to enable the whole team to approach each of the three stages in a proper state of mind and with all the equipment required at the ready.

The very first occasion in which this new operation was carried out was one of intense drama. The first and second stages were completed satisfactorily and each wound was closed. The big problem was whether the stomach would come up into the neck in the third phase and what would happen if it failed to do so.

With trepidation the root of the neck was opened up and the upper end of the gullet identified amongst the vital structures at this site. The gullet was gently pulled up into the neck and at this time the whole atmosphere of the theatre was tense and silent. Slowly, the gullet came up and then the growth came into view and was pulled clear. A final gentle pull on the gullet brought the stomach into the neck and the dome of the fundus of the stomach popped up into the wound like an inflated balloon. There was a moment of total silence and then the first assistant (the son of a famous neurosurgeon) suddenly let out a shout of joy and began to cheer.

There was a feeling of great achievement that the concept of total removal of the gullet could be followed by its replacement by the stomach brought up into the neck. But at this time I never contemplated in my wildest dreams that this new operation would attain such recognition and would open up a new phase in the treatment of oesophageal cancer and would lead to travel and lecturing throughout the whole world in the years which lay ahead.

As time went on the procedure became routine and to ease the strain it seemed appropriate that a tea break should separate each of the three phases, to allow a short period of rest and re-adjustment for all the staff.

At my own hospital a nurse would produce a cup of tea between each of the three phases and this was done without ceremony and without comment.

However, some years later when I was demonstrating this operation for the first time in Barcelona, by the kind invitation of Dr Curto-Cardus, with a large group of Spanish surgeons watching the procedure, I had an amusing and pleasant experience.

After phase one was completed a waiter in a sterile gown but with a black bow tie arrived with my tea on a silver tray. After the second phase of the operation a repeat performance occurred and on this occasion he produced a small paella, presumably to sustain me after all my efforts.

After several years' experience of this operation the great advantages of the technique became even more clear. It was now the time to publish a well tried technique, but in view of its complexity, emphasis must be paid to the practical aspects of the operation. Contrary to the usual practice it was decided to produce a film of the operation before actually producing a paper for inclusion in the surgical literature.

Accordingly, a film was made with the help of Ronald Ridley* and Dr R. A. Goodhead† from the Department of Audiovisual Aids in the Postgraduate Institute in Newcastle. The film was shown in London in 1969 and won the British Medical Association Silver Award.[19] A publication was made in 1972 in the Annals of the Royal College of Surgeons of England and resulted in the award of an Hunterian Professorship.[20]

Subsequently as the series of cases increased many publications have been made in the surgical journals.[20, 21] So widely accepted are these operative techniques evolved in Darlington that chapters on oesophageal cancer have been contributed to standard textbooks published throughout the world, the most recent having just been published in London in 1992.[22]

As frequently happens in other walks of life, investigation of a special problem leads to the solution of other, apparently unrelated problems, and so it was with research into oesophageal cancer. Some aspects of absorption of fluids from the mouth became apparent which were helpful in other spheres of surgery and especially in the management of post operative cases.[22] Similarly the mode of healing of parts of the intestinal

---

* Ronald Ridley, Senior Photographer
† Dr R. A. Goodhead, T.D., Producer, Audiovisual Aids Dept., Newcastle Postgraduate Medical Institute

tract was emphasized. These findings formed the basis of the Ernest Miles Memorial Lecture held at the Annual Meeting of the European Society of Surgical Oncology in Liverpool in 1990.[23, 24]

In addition to these two major projects, that of peptic ulcer and that of oesophageal cancer, there was one other project of considerable importance.

There is a peculiar disease of the colon which often affects young patients, especially women, but unfortunately the cause is still not fully understood. It is called ulcerative colitis and may be present as an acute fulminant life threatening condition, or in a more chronic form where the health of the patient is slowly undermined.

In severe cases the treatment is surgical and involves removing the whole colon and the back passage. This necessitates the provision of a bowel opening in the abdominal wall which is called an ileostomy. One of the very first cases encountered in the Friarage Hospital was in 1950 and was just such a case of the acute fulminant type. The surgical registrar who operated on the patient in the first instance had established an ileostomy as an emergency procedure but had not removed the colon.

The patient's condition continued to be grave and it was decided that the colon should be removed. This was duly carried out but, at operation, the patient's condition was so poor that the rectum was left for removal at a later date when the patient's condition had improved. She left the hospital with a view to re-admission for removal of the rectal stump.

During this period, though her general health had improved enormously, the rectal stump continued to discharge blood and pus indicating that the rectal stump was still diseased and should be removed.

The patient was adverse to this since it required the provision of a permanent ileostomy and she was insistent that she wanted her bowel to be restored to the normal state. She was told that this was not advisable as the rectum would continue to cause trouble. However, on the night before her admission to hospital she felt that she could not face a permanent ileostomy and she attempted suicide.

Her general practitioner, Dr Kenneth Easton* of Catterick was a man

---

* Dr Kenneth Easton, O.B.E., G.P., Catterick, North Yorkshire

of outstanding ability. He had, while in the R.A.F., helped to deal with the inmates of Buchenwald, Belsen and Dachau, and had in recent years established a scheme for immediate medical assistance at the site of road traffic accidents. His reputation in this field is national and international.

Dr Easton called for an immediate family and medical conference. After much discussion it was decided to accede to the patient's request to remove the ileostomy and to restore the use of the rectum. She was duly re-admitted and the small bowel was joined to the diseased rectum, an operation called ileo-rectal anastomosis. To the astonishment of all, her progress was excellent and the inflamed rectal stump began to heal and she returned to normal.

In subsequent years she had a family of two and is still alive and well. So far as I am aware this was the first case of ileo-rectal anastomosis carried out for ulcerative colitis.

In subsequent years over twenty such cases have been carried out in Northallerton and Darlington and many were demonstrated when Surgical Societies, including the Moynihan Surgical Club visited the Friarage hospital. The operation is now recognized as a valuable procedure in the treatment in special cases of ulcerative colitis.

In the most recent years a research project has just been completed concerning the occurrence of multiple primary cancers.[25] In the past, great attention has been paid to the grading and staging of malignant tumours, and these are used as an index of prognosis.

I realized for some time, however, that while in the vast majority of cases this information gives a reasonably accurate outlook, yet there are cases in the good groups that do badly and some in the bad groups that do well. It may well be that in the past too much attention has been paid to the tumour and too little to the patient's defence mechanism.

This work draws attention to the defence mechanisms of the body against cancer and it may well be that the newspaper headlines about patients *fighting* cancer may be truer than the journalists realize.

The importance of clinical research in a District General Hospital is two fold. In the first instance the results of this research give practical guidelines in regard to the treatment of diseases but secondly it also indicates a completely new trend and emphasis in clinical practice since the establishment of the District General Hospitals. In former years virtually all research projects were carried out at the Teaching Hospitals where the brain power and the laboratory facilities were located.

Since the advent of the National Health Service and its decentralizing effects, talents and skills have been dispersed from the Teaching Hospital to the District General Hospitals where the major part of clinical practice is now carried out. It is therefore to be expected that clinical research should be carried out at these District Hospitals and this requires further financial support.

At the same time it must also be fully realized that the Teaching Hospitals will still be the leaders in scientific research and advance, since the facilities are centred in these institutions whose records and tradition are of outstanding merit. In London the clinical load in the Teaching Hospitals has been greatly reduced but the research capabilities have been increased.

The most recent report by Sir Bernard Tomlinson suggests the closing of some London Teaching Hospital and this may imperil the continued research activities of these centres of excellence.

Recent changes in philosophy in the National Health Service may however also contribute to decline in clinical research. Free market forces have been recently introduced into the National Health Service where medical treatment may be purchased by a Health Authority in a price competitive market. This may have unforeseen and far reaching effects on clinical research.

The complex major operations for the removal of a cancer of the gullet in an old man may not provide a commercially viable project. It would be commercially more profitable to repair ten hernias in young men rather than operate on a cancer of the gullet in a man of seventy-five.

In entering on a market economy in health services the human face of medicine and its caring image is in grave danger of being impaired. Under the new managerial system which has now been introduced, a lay manager under the pressure of a restricted budget will opt for the cheapest option. This is likely to be in conflict with the clinician whose ethos is more patient orientated and humanitarian in the tradition of the medical profession.

It seems unlikely that the advances made in the treatment of cancer of the oesophagus over the period of about thirty years in the Northallerton and Darlington areas could have been possible under the financial systems so recently introduced into the hospital service.

It is particularly important in medical problems, where an alteration of procedure can have unexpected consequences, that a "pilot scheme" should be introduced before any major changes are made. In the scientific field, experiment is in the forefront of real progress. Unfortunately under pressure of political influences, such essential experiments have not been carried out and untried schemes are now being implemented in medical fields with serious consequences which have not been foreseen. Similar neglect to use "pilot schemes" in other fields have lead to great trouble and embarrassment in social life and in commerce, and these have resulted in changes of policy now referred to as U-turns in political circles.

THE WAITING LIST

In most recent times great political attention has been directed to the size of waiting lists, both for out-patient appointments and in-patient treatment. The size of the waiting list or the waiting time is now being used as a measure of performance. In Darlington and Northallerton these problems were dealt with formerly as efficiently as the financial allocation would allow.

Secretarial assistance in the Out-Patient Department and the use of the block booking system enabled the Out-Patient Clinics to be very large and yet to run efficiently. Urgent cases were seen at the next clinic and though this meant that some patients had unexpectedly to wait, waiting times were generally acceptable. The availability of Consultant Services enabled a vast number of patients suffering from a wide variety of diseases to have advice and treatment that was not previously available. Inevitably the waiting lists increased and a massive hospital expansion was initiated in Darlington, a programme that took fifteen years to complete.

Each week the Ward Sister, the Surgical Registrar, and the Consultant would go over the waiting list. The selection of patients for admission was made on grounds of clinical need and urgency and on the beds available at the time. A minor case such as varicose veins would not take priority over a serious problem simply because of the length of time that it had been on the waiting list. There were no financial considerations, and the word budget was never heard. The surgeons who provided the greater skills and patient care often had longer waiting lists.

In those days patients were kept in hospital much longer than is the practice today, and when they were discharged from hospital they were able to look after themselves with minimal nursing or medical support at home. This practice certainly contributed to the length of the waiting lists. No financial rewards or inducements were offered to any of the lay staff as an encouragement to reduce waiting lists as is the case today.

Quality of care was of paramount importance and political or financial influences were not at this time a consideration. There was never any administrative pressure to influence or interfere with the admission or clinical management of patients. Compared with the present time these were indeed halcyon days.

16

"Emergency Ward Ten"

IN every walk of life emergencies arise, but in medical practice the occurrence of emergencies is a very important problem. Most emergencies are accommodated as part of the normal work load and often with minimal disruption of the usual routine. There are however occasions when an emergency is unusual and has some special connotations so that it stands out in the memory. Some of these special emergencies are worth recording.

On one occasion while operating at the Memorial Hospital in Darlington I got an urgent call to the Friarage Hospital about a patient who had been admitted in emergency.

The patient stated that he had been eating hay and that the hay had become stuck in his throat so that he was no longer able to swallow. X-ray of the chest did not show anything of note but X-ray of the abdomen showed that the stomach was full of a large number of strange objects. So remarkable was the appearance that one of the registrars described the swallowed objects as being like The Old Curiosity Shop. A dinner knife and an old safety razor blade with three holes could easily be identified among the large number of objects. He was operated on and in addition to a stomach full of hay, there was the broken dinner knife, the Gillette razor blade, a broken cup, a metal punch, a protractor, a key, a pen nib, two screws, a kirby grip, a pin, three stones and a variety of coins (Fig. 12).

This strange collection of objects was removed from the stomach but the day following operation the patient passed in his motion a domino which appropriately happened to be the double six. Recovery from his

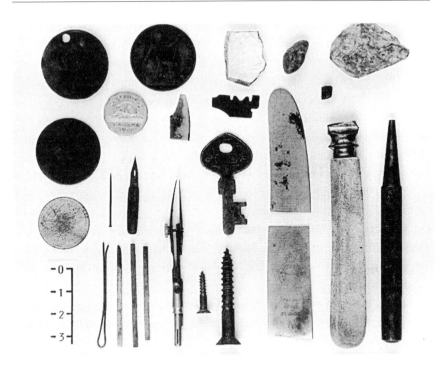

FIGURE 12. *A strange collection of objects swallowed by a patient and removed from the stomach at emergency operation.*

stomach operation was excellent but it was his mind that required the real attention.

Night calls are tiresome and inevitable in the life of a surgeon and come to be regarded as part of his normal work. A night call takes on a special significance however if the emergency case involves one's own colleagues, as happened when I got a telephone call at 2 a.m.

The call came from Dr D. M. McKenzie of Northallerton who reported that his partner Dr J. O. M. Wedderburn has been found by a police patrol, lying on the road on top of a "car door" on the road near a little village called Yafforth, a mile or two from Northallerton.

In actual fact the "car door" was the sunshine roof of his Sunbeam Talbot car and he had apparently been projected through the roof of the car and had landed on the road with the sunshine roof lying below him. The strange feature was that there was no trace of his car. When daylight came the car was discovered in an adjacent field into which it had careered and come to rest quite a distance from the road.

Dr Wedderburn was in general practice in Northallerton but was very interested in anaesthesia and did in fact do one of my surgical operating lists at the Friarage Hospital as already mentioned.

When I examined him at the hospital he had a compound fracture of the front of his skull and amongst other injuries a fracture of his femur. He had the compound fracture of the skull dealt with in the usual lines, and soon regained consciousness so that his femur could be dealt with.

His recovery was complete but it is sad to say that some years later he was killed in an equally unusual accident while travelling in London. He was driving a shooting brake which was stationary at traffic lights when another car ran into the back of him. A heavy trunk in the back of the shooting brake was projected forward striking him on the head and causing fatal injuries.

The majority of emergency cases were dealt with in hospital but there were rare occasions where for special reasons the patient had to be seen outside hospital. There were two such cases each of which was rather special but for different reasons.

The first was a farmer who had taken ill in his remote farm high up in the Pennine Hills between Swaledale and Wensleydale. It was late in the evening when the call came to my home at Croft.

(Croft is a little village on the river Tees renowned because it was where Lewis Carrol wrote *Alice in Wonderland*. Lewis Carrol was the pen name of the author who was called Charles Lutwidge Dodgson, the son of the vicar who lived in the local rectory on the other side of the river opposite my home.)

I set out in heavy rain and took the back road which passes through the village of Middleton Tyas on the way to Scotch Corner. I passed through a little valley near by where a brook overflows on to the road when the weather has been wet. When I reached Scotch Corner the rain had turned to sleet and by the time I reached the ancient town of Richmond snow was falling heavily. Taking the road to Leyburn I drove up the hills that lie between Swaledale and Wensleydale and finally located the farm on a remote hill side.

The farmer was suffering from an abscess in the abdomen alongside his colon (paracolic abscess) which had resulted from a disease of the colon known as diverticulitis.

In such inclement weather, and for other domestic considerations, I felt that this problem could be managed at the patient's home with the co-operation of the general practitioner in a practice where the standard of care was so characteristically high.

Setting off in thick snow on the homeward journey, as I came down from the hills the snow changed to sleet and by the time I reached the little brook near Middleton Tyas, rain was pouring down and the brook which had overflowed onto the road had changed into quite a torrent. Unfortunately, I crossed the stream at high speed and, with the impact, water was forced up under the bonnet of the car and the engine stalled just before I had reached the other side of the stream.

There was nothing to be done but to wait until the engine had dried out. While waiting I saw another car coming along the road and got out in the pouring rain to warn the driver of the flood. He slowed down and crossed the flood carefully, waved his hand, and slowly continued his journey leaving me still stuck by the roadside. It was after midnight and I decided to wait in the car until morning rather than walk miles in the pouring rain to the nearest phone box.

After some hours of waiting, at about 4 a.m., I saw the lights of an approaching car and once again got out to warn the driver of the flood but on this occasion my warning was not really necessary. To my astonishment it was the same car that had passed hours previously but on this occasion the car stopped. The farmer driver explained that when he got home and went to bed he was unable to sleep thinking that he had left me stuck by the roadside after I had been kind enough to warn him of the danger.

After some hours of sleeplessness he decided to get up and bring a tow-rope and I was duly and thankfully rescued. The experience emphasized that consultant practice in Yorkshire is very different from that in London.

The next most memorable case was an out-patient in every sense of the term. It was a Friday evening and my wife and I were preparing for a visit to London the following day. It was mid-winter and the snow was beginning to fall. While listening to the nine o'clock news to get the weather forecast for our journey the following day there was an urgent ringing of the front door bell.

On the doorstep there was an anxious man who asked if I could come to the scene of an accident at the Croft Working Mens Club about a quarter of a mile from my home. Apparently they could not get hold of any doctor, and so I rushed out on foot to see a sight that in some ways reminded me of the London blitz. There were firemen and flashing lights everywhere and all the paraphernalia of a major accident.

A very large lorry coming down the hill from Hurworth had failed to negotiate a bend and had ploughed straight into the front of the Club. The building had collapsed on the cab of the lorry and the driver was trapped inside.

My first reaction was that the lorry should be pulled out allowing the building to collapse completely and the driver to be freed by a rescue party standing by. I was assured however that the Borough Engineer and the Borough Surveyor had both visited the site and had given instructions that the lorry should not be moved. By the time I had got to the site of the accident both had gone home and, in such inclement weather, who could blame them.

With a great deal of difficulty I was able to get into the drivers cab to reach the driver but, as the space was so small, I had to remove my overcoat and jacket to enable me to do so.

The driver's body was trapped from the level of the chest downwards and he was in agony with both legs crushed between the front panel of the lorry and the gearbox. The problem was to sedate him while the long process of freeing him began. Only his head and his hands were free, so it seemed appropriate to give him an injection of pain relieving pethidine into the veins on the back of his hands. This enabled the firemen to insert chocks and to begin the long and painful process of wedging the metal structures apart and beginning to free his body.

At first it was reasonably warm in the cab while the engine was hot, but as the night proceeded it got colder and colder. I was immensely impressed by the Darlington Fire Service who patiently and skilfully inserted the wedges and slowly began to free the driver. When any major procedure was about to be carried out I would climb back into the cab and using the patient's wrist-watch as a tourniquet was able to distend the veins on the back of the hand enabling me to inject pain killing drugs.

All of us got colder and colder as the east wind blew strongly and the snow fell through the remnants of the building. While all this was going on in arctic conditions, I could visualize the Borough Engineer and the Borough Surveyor comfortably tucked up in a warm bed.

Strangely enough, not a single resident came to help but at 3 a.m. a soup kitchen arrived and I have never had such a welcome drink of hot soup in my entire life. Clutching the soup dish like a hot-water bottle and sipping its contents was a most heart and body warming experience which regrettably did not last for long.

Intravenous injection requires warm hands and a delicate touch, but as time went on I was becoming so cold that I could not accomplish this task. Below the club there was a cellar where I was told there was a coke fire and so decided to go down and get warm enough to continue my work.

The sight in the cellar was quite fantastic. The front wheels of the lorry were sticking through the ceiling of the cellar and on a bench below the wheels was a man lying flat on his back, sound asleep, and with his hat perched over the front of his face. He had obviously visited the club earlier in the evening and had retired to the cellar where he was sleeping off the effects of too much beer.

I had to disturb him to get to the stove and as I did so he woke up, took off his hat from his face and stared with incredulous eyes at the lorry wheels protruding through the ceiling above his head. His face was a study of astonishment. He suddenly realized the position, got up looking dazed and slowly walked from the cellar like a zombie. I have never seen him from that day to this.

Returning to the cab injections were repeated and the freeing process recommenced. It was getting on to dawn but still the drivers right leg was firmly trapped and it was then apparent that he was wearing a type of wellington boot. His general condition was beginning to deteriorate quite rapidly and he became shocked and pale and looked as though he might die.

I decided that we would have to amputate his leg to get him free in time and so I sent for my Surgical Registrar, Mr Brian Hayes* who

---

* Brian Hayes, F.R.C.S., F.R.C.S.E., now Consultant Surgeon, East Glamorgan Hospital, Pontyprydd

worked with me at the Memorial Hospital. He came out fully armed and equipped with all that was necessary to amputate the leg under local anaesthesia.

As a preliminary I felt I should perhaps cut off his boot to clear a site for amputation. By the greatest good fortune when I cut away part of the boot with an amputation knife, I was able to free his leg and thereby amputation of his leg was thankfully avoided. By this time television cameras had arrived mysteriously while Brian Hayes and I pulled the driver free from his cab. He was taken by ambulance to Darlington Memorial Hospital where he was admitted under my care.

Exhausted and numb with the cold after hours in the snow I walked home at about 8.00 a.m. and went fast asleep in a hot bath. I was disturbed at about 11.00 a.m. by the telephone which was by the side of my bath. It was the police and they wanted to know if I had taken the driver's watch! I cannot repeat what I said to the police constable.

The survival of this patient was quite remarkable in view of his crush injuries and of being held in the vertical position in the extreme cold throughout the night. I was to learn later that he was a fitness fanatic who used to run in a special annual race where the contestants run from Reeth to the top of a local hill in a type of marathon run. I heard subsequently that he was able to continue as a competitor, but strangely enough never heard further from him.

In medicine it is expected that what is unexpected is the thing that is likely to happen, and so it was one Friday afternoon. I had just completed a very long operating list at the Friarage and had just arrived home when I was called back to the hospital.

The theatre sister who had helped me all day had been travelling home in her open M.G. Midget, and unfortunately was involved in a road traffic accident. She had been brought into the Casualty Department and was quite conscious but suffering from severe facial injuries. I set about suturing the wounds under local anaesthesia and in the course of this procedure she complained of feeling funny and a feeling of weakness down one side. I noted on looking at her eyes that one pupil had contracted to pinpoint size and that she had a slight weakness down one side.

The diagnosis of ruptured middle meningeal artery – the type of injury sometimes sustained by boxers – seemed obvious and emergency operation was urgently required. At this time the nearest neurosurgical unit was at Newcastle General Hospital and the journey along the old A1 was both slow and unpredictable and most patients were unsaveable by the time they had reached this special unit.

As I had carried out the type of operation required many times during the war, I had Sister taken to the main operating theatre, opened her skull and removed the clot from her brain and tied the artery. Her recovery was dramatic but in view of the fact that she was one of our key staff I felt that she should be checked by a consultant neurologist. I rang an old friend of mine, Dr Henry Miller* who was the Senior Neurologist at the Royal Victoria Infirmary Newcastle and he agreed to come and check that all was well.

It so happened that he and his wife were due to dine with a Mr & Mrs. Hankinson that very evening. Mr Hankinson† was a research neurosurgeon and was soon to become Professor of Neurosurgery at the university. I suggested that the venue for dinner should be changed to the Croft Spa Hotel which would provide the opportunity for a joint consultation and not interfere with his social arrangement. This was readily agreed to and Joan and the two wives waited at the hotel while the three of us went to see the theatre sister. The consultation was short and, as all was going well, we started dinner in good time.

As a raconteur Henry Miller was quite superb. Hankinson seemed to catalyse his humour and the two of them provided perhaps the most amusing evening I have ever known. Henry told his stories which were quite superb and the whole restaurant seemed to join in the mirth.

His final story was about a famous neurosurgeon who insisted that all patients for examination should be completely stripped. On one occasion he was called by a general practitioner to see a patient who was an attractive young lady. The neurosurgeon followed his usual practice and the patient was duly completely undressed. In the middle of the consultation he

---

* Dr Henry Miller F.R.C.P., Senior Neurologist, Royal Victoria Infirmary, Newcastle-upon-Tyne.

† Mr Hankinson, F.R.C.S., Consultant Neurosurgeon, Royal Victoria Hospital, Newcastle-upon-Tyne

realized that he had not brought his ophthalmoscope to examine the retina and the interior parts of the eye. He left the room to go to his car for the instrument, but ageing as he was, when he opened the doors of his Rolls Royce conditioned reflexes took over. He got into the car and drove off home to be greeted by frantic messages from the general practitioner to return to the consultation as the patient was still naked!

Emergency surgery is often life saving and yet it is not always carried out by surgeons of the greatest experience. It is interesting to contemplate that there is a similarity between the situations that occurred in war and those that still occur in times of peace. In war the most experienced surgeons were rightly protected and did not always do emergency surgery in situations of great risk and emergency work was carried out by junior surgeons.

Similarly, in peacetime emergency surgery is often carried out by the less experienced surgeons but for a very different reason. With the heavy burden of work in the District General Hospital it is not desirable for a surgeon to operate all day and yet to do emergencies throughout the night. To provide for the dealing with emergency surgery at consultant level requires a significant increase in the consultant surgical staff. Strange to relate the Department of Health or the Government of the day has never grasped this reality until just now. Over the years administrative staff has increased enormously, as though stimulated by some secret growth hormone, while emphasis on the clinical and related staff has been, and still is, neglected.

Emergency surgery is dramatic and exciting and builds surgical character. It is, however, a young surgeon's *métier*, and to involve the more senior consultant in these duties will impair the ordinary routine work of any surgical unit. Government thinking on these matters appears to be a little confused.

Emergency problems pervade the entire professional life of a surgeon, and these have to do with patients and their problems. There was however one very unusual emergency which had nothing whatever to do with surgical practice or with any family problems. It concerned dining with the Queen on the Royal Yacht *Britannia* when she visited Teesport. Joan and I had the honour to be invited to dinner and the invitation was a command rather than an invitation.

The invitation was precise in timing and was 7.55 p.m. for 8.00 p.m.

To ensure that there would be no problems we rehearsed and timed the journey from our home in Hurworth to the dock at Teesport.

On the special day, however we found ourselves considerably in advance of the time, and my secretary and her husband who were driving us decided that we should make a little detour towards Redcar so that our arrival would be precise. Unfortunately, after the detour traffic had suddenly built up we found ourselves in a traffic jam and in great danger of being late. This was quite an appalling thought and I became very concerned.

I had, however, been previously instructed that if there were any problems to put a special sticker on the windscreen of the car and this would facilitate my journey. This is certainly what happened. As soon as the sticker was in place a police patrolman took over and we were escorted with flashing blue lights through all the traffic and arrived at the quayside just on time. This seemed to be a very special way of dealing with an emergency though no lives were at stake.

The experience of dinner on the Royal Yacht was quite unique. To walk along the red carpet to the gangway and to be escorted by a surgeon commander on board was a wonderful experience.

Presentation of a score of guests to the Queen was a most memorable occasion. To dine with the silverware of Drake and Hawkins is an experience of a lifetime. To stand on the deck with the Royal party in the flood-lights and to see and hear the band of the Royal Marines play, while the crowds, scarcely seen because of the glare of the flood-lights, cheered the Queen and the Duke of Edinburgh, was a fantastic experience.

All wonderful experiences come to an end and when we were driven from the elegance of the Royal Yacht into the crowds one felt that one was passing from the highlight of life into oblivion. And so ended perhaps our most memorable occasion.

17

Surgical Visitors

HERE in the North, in this new environment, I found great freedom, and the interest and the volume of the surgical work far exceeded my most sanguine expectations. There was, however, deep in my mind a feeling of loss at leaving London where there were so many people and so many professional contacts. It was this feeling of isolation which impaired to some degree the joy of working in an ideal surgical unit. At this time I looked forward to my visits to London which I still regarded as my surgical home and wondered if it would ever come about that surgeons would want to visit Darlington, in the same way as they would want to come to London. This was a situation that was to be realized far sooner than could ever have been anticipated.

The first surgeons to visit the unit at the Friarage Hospital were the regional surgical visitors from Newcastle Regional Hospital Board. The visit was a supervisory one and was carried out by Professor Pybus and Professor Bentley. Professor Pybus was the Emeritus Professor of Surgery at Newcastle-upon-Tyne, and Professor Bentley was the newly appointed professor who had come to Newcastle after the completion of his service as a lieutenant-colonel in the Royal Army Medical Corps. Professor Pybus had been on the committee that had appointed me, and I had met Professor Bentley at York Military Hospital when we were both in the service, and he too was a member of the appointments committee.

Knowing that Professor Bentley had been an officer in charge of a surgical division of the army, the visit was arranged on somewhat military lines, just like a commanding officers inspection of a surgical unit.

At each ward the staff were on parade and nothing was amiss. Professor

Bentley seemed delighted with the arrangement as it no doubt reminded him of his former glories.

Professor Pybus, however, appeared to be extremely irritated and seemed to resent the ordered structure of his visit. He was shown a large range of interesting surgical cases but in spite of this he continued to appear displeased. He even seemed to resent the great numbers of duodenal ulcer cases that had been operated on most successfully, and gave me the impression that he believed that such cases should only be operated on in the Teaching Hospital.

This professor's major interest seemed to focus on one minor case, a middle aged man who had a hydrocele (a fluid sac round the testicle) which had been operated on. He asked me why I had operated on him, and would it not have been better to inject the hydrocele with a sclerosing fluid. I was rather surprised at his enquiry since the method of treatment given to this patient was entirely orthodox and generally accepted in surgical circles. He pursued his criticism with such persistence and vehemence that I felt considerably disturbed and irritated. In defence of my treatment I felt that he should be told of the experience of a senior surgeon at King's College Hospital in London, who under the pressure of war circumstances, had treated a case of hydrocele by the injection of sclerosing fluid as Pybus was now advocating. And so I outlined to him the experience I had gained from this special incident.

In London, with the strict rationing of petrol during the war, many surgeons at King's College travelled by tram from the hospital at Denmark Hill, to their consulting rooms in Harley Street. Just after finishing his Out-Patient Clinic Mr Yates-Bell,* the senior urologist, left the hospital and took a tram to travel into central London. He sat behind a man who had just left his Out-Patient clinic after having his hydrocele injected and was obviously in great pain. He was twisting from side to side and had both hands cupped over his groin. He was groaning aloud and swearing that if he ever again met the surgeon who had injected his hydrocele he would give him a real beating. Concealing his identity Yates-Bell left the tram at the next stop, gratefully still unrecognized.

The effect of this story on the professor was dramatic, he went silent

---

* Mr J. G. Yates-Bell, Senior Urologist, King's College Hospital, London.

and virtually never spoke another word or made another comment. Even the ward tea served by an attractive sister did not arouse him from his gloom. It was then that I realized why, because of his behaviour and attitude, he was known to the resident surgical staff as "Piggy" Pybus. Professor Bentley seemed immensely amused by the whole episode.

Future visits were of a very different character and were made out of interest in the surgical treatment of dyspepsia and of cancer of the gullet. The surgical assessors were soon to change and Professor Pybus was replaced by Professor Hamilton Barclay and later by Professor Norman Hodgson. These also were former Professors of Surgery in Newcastle and it was a delight to entertain them on the very many occasions they visited the Friarage Hospital. They were a great source of encouragement to me in the development of many of my surgical interests.

On one occasion Professor Norman Hodgson, who had been the first assistant to the famous Professor Grey Turner, was watching an operation for the removal of a cancer of the middle-third of the gullet. He kept pressing closer to get a better view of this new technique that I was developing. He kept muttering "my, my" at a time when I was dissecting the gullet off the auricular part of the heart and the great veins entering the heart at this point.

As the technique was new, I was a little worried in case he disapproved of what I was doing and that was why he kept muttering under his breath.

While having a cup of tea after the operation I asked him what comments he was making during the procedure and he explained the position much to my relief. He told me that while he was watching the pulmonary veins (the large vein entering the heart) being dissected free of the gullet he at last understood why some of the cases operated on by Grey Turner using a "blind technique" died of torrential haemorrhage.

At this time, in the 1930s, opening of the chest cavity was dangerous and to avoid doing this in an old patient with cancer of the gullet, Grey Turner had devised a special technique for operation. He opened the abdomen and freed the lower end of the gullet and then opened the neck and freed the upper end of the gullet. Then working from above downwards in the neck, and from below upwards in the abdomen, the gullet was freed and pulled out in what is described as a "blind technique". It was obvious that, in some cases where great veins were stuck onto the growth, that in pulling out the gullet these veins would be torn wide open and cause such severe haemorrhage that death would take place in a matter of moments. It is remarkable that an American surgeon has resurrected this "blind" technique after an interval of over half a century.[26]

Professor Hamilton Barclay's visits were also a delight, and he seemed very impressed with the clinical research project on peptic ulcer. He asked me to report my results at a meeting of the North of England Surgical Society which had recently been formed in Newcastle-upon-Tyne. This was my first lecture given outside London and I was delighted to be invited to address the Society.

In due course this Society met in Darlington when Mr David Dickson* of Teesside was President, when a large operative session was carried out. To accommodate the members, wooden platforms and scaffolding were erected in the operating theatres by the hospital carpenters and the structures covered with green surgical towels to create the right ambience.

The operative techniques demonstrated at this session were, of course, recorded in the surgical address which followed the operative session. I felt at this visit that the work in Darlington had started in earnest. The visit of the North of England Surgical Society was the first of many surgical societies that were to come to Darlington Memorial Hospital in subsequent years.

It is said among surgeons that when attending a surgical conference, it is not only the major papers that are presented which are of value. Of even more importance are the individual contacts and discussions that take place outside the conference hall.

The visits of individual surgeons to the unit has indeed been a source of great interest and I believe of great importance. In the decade 1967–77 a very large number of surgeons from all over the world visited the units in Darlington and at the Friarage Hospital, Northallerton. The importance of events are not always appreciated at the time and gain their true importance in retrospect.

At first, due to lack of insight and appreciation of the importance of these surgical visitors a register was not kept. However, after the

---

* David Dickson, F.R.C.S.E., Surgeon, Teesside Group of Hospitals.

institution of a register over 190 individual surgeons from every continent visited the unit.

It was the custom for visitors to stay for periods varying from days to even as long as weeks, so that during their stay every aspect of the work could be studied. While some of the visitors were accomodated in the hospital, many stayed at my home. I would like to pay special tribute to my wife Joan who looked after the guests with great care and attention, and I am most grateful to her.

The Out-Patient Department provided a great interest (Fig. 13) only excelled by the demonstrations in the operating theatre. There is something quite fascinating in discussing each individual case with surgeons from different countries and with different cultures and different academic backgrounds.

Of the many distinguished visitors several stand out for a variety of reasons. It is rewarding to recall these various personalities. The first to be mentioned is Professor "Bob" Macbeth who was Professor of Surgery

FIGURE 13. *Visiting surgeons at the author's unit at Darlington Memorial Hospital. Front (left to right): Professor Imrie, Professor of Surgery, Vienna; Prof. Gavriolou Dan, Bucharest; Author; Mr Ronald Wiles, Australia; Mr Andrew W. Jowett, Wolverhampton. Back (left to right): Surgeon from Sri Lanka; Mr Paul Farell, Eire; Eileen Raine, Secretary; Sister Dellbridge, Out-Patient Sister.*

in Edmonton, Alberta. His name is a household word in Canada and he is very well known in many parts of the world. (Fig. 14). He came to Darlington on the recommendation of Professor Welbourn, Professor of Surgery at the London Postgraduate Medical School at Hammersmith Hospital.

Much to my delight and that of my colleagues he stayed at the unit for several weeks. His interest extended to every aspect of the work carried out in Darlington and Northallerton. He was a brilliant person and felt that his colleagues in Canada would

FIGURE 14. *Professor 'Bob' Macbeth, Professor of Surgery in Edmonton, Alberta.*

be interested in the work he had seen in Darlington. Accordingly, in due course, he arranged for me to make a lecture tour of Canada to include Edmonton, Calgary, Saskatchewan and Vancouver.

One of the most unusual visitors to Darlington was Professor Gavriliou Dan from Bucharest. He had a very special interest in oesophageal surgery and in the construction of gastric tubes to replace the gullet. He was coming to England at the invitation of the Royal College of Surgeons of England to give the Moynihan Lecture at the University of Leeds. He was anxious to visit my Unit and, as I was surgical adviser to the Royal College in the Newcastle region, I was requested by the President of the College to look after him.

It was arranged that he should fly from London to Teesside where he was to be met. As I had heard a great deal about him but had never seen even his photograph, I wondered if I would be able to recognize him.

This however, presented no difficulties for, as he came down the gangway from the aircraft, he was wearing a large green and yellow rosette, such as is worn by football fans, with his name inscribed in large letters in the centre of the rosette. He was a most interesting and practical surgeon with whom I had so much in common, and his visit was a great success.

After his stay in Darlington I took him to the Moynihan Club meeting in Manchester where I was the President, and after this meeting sent him off to Leeds where, by a strange coincidence, he was to give the Moynihan Lecture at the Leeds General Infirmary.

The variety of visitors added interest, and Spanish surgeons were frequent guests. Professor Miguel from Valladolid near Madrid was a frequent visitor and had a special interest in a grafting operative technique for the repair of hernias. From South Africa Miss Mannell came to work in the unit for a year. She is now a leading surgeon in Johannesburg and works in the famous Baraguanath Hospital where the casualties of the racial struggle in South Africa are dealt with. (Fig. 15)

It is the custom of the Royal College of Surgeons of England to elect distinguished overseas surgeons to the appointment of Sims Professors.

FIGURE 15. *Surgical Out-Patient Clinic.*
Eileen Raine, Secretary; Professor Miguel, Spain; the author; Miss Mannell, Baraguanath Hospital, South Africa; Sister Dellbridge.

This appointment gives them the opportunity to travel to various centres in Britain over a period of a year. I had the privilege of entertaining two of these professors in my Unit in Darlington. The first was Sir John Loewenthal from Sidney, Australia and the second was Professor Salter from Toronto in Canada.

Professor Loewenthal spent a week seeing clinical work and then suddenly one Saturday morning while sitting in my clinic he said he would like to see a First Division football match.

I was quite surprised at this request and a little anxious that I would not be able to make appropriate arrangements at such short notice. I suddenly remembered that I had an old friend, Bobby Rutherford, who was a surgeon in Newcastle and was on the Board of the Newcastle United Football Club. I rang him right away and with unbelievable speed he made arrangements for us to go to Newcastle that afternoon to attend a match between Newcastle United and West Ham Football Club.

We arrived at St. James' Park and were greeted by a uniformed official who directed us up to the Directors' Box while a colleague of his parked my car.

It was quite an occasion, as a former Newcastle player (Bobby Robson) had just been transferred from Newcastle to West Ham Football Club and this made the match of special interest and provided the keenest competition. Hoping to make a good impression of English sportsmanship with Sir John, I was greatly embarrassed to sit in the Directors' Box and hear the language of some of the spectators. Fortunately, in the Geordie accent of Tyneside most of it was unintelligible. Much to my relief Sir John was immensely amused and thoroughly enjoyed his last afternoon in the North East.

The other Sims Professor was Professor Salter from Canada. He was a prodigious worker and commandeered my office in my home from 5 a.m. until 7.30 a.m. when I got up. During this time he prepared his lectures and speeches for the ensuing day. He was a superb lecturer and a very quick wit. As a farewell to his visit to the North East my friends in Newcastle decided to take him to a popular function in those days known as a Medieval Banquet.

At these banquets a guest of honour is elected to be the Baron and so it befell to Professor Salter to make a speech after the dinner. In truly medieval style mead was drunk in profusion and there was much mirth and laughter in the great hall at Lumley Castle. I wondered how the Professor would make his speech in such revelry and din.

At the appropriate time he rose slowly to his feet and waited for quietness before beginning his talk. His speech was superb.

He explained that he had just crossed the great sea from the New World but his barque had encountered adverse winds and was consequently delayed. He continued to speak in the tones and demeanour of Queen Elizabeth the First and held everyone absolutely spellbound. At the end of half an hour of complete silence the applause was thunderous and a host of revellers clamoured forward to get his autograph. It was a most successful termination to his visit to the Newcastle region.

Perhaps the most domesticated visitor was John Wong* who was a graduate of the University of Sidney but who was then first assistant to Professor G. B. Ong† at the Queen Mary's Hospital in Hong Kong. He spent much time at the hospital watching the three-phase operation for removal of cancer of the gullet and when not doing so was a most helpful guest at our home. His excellence has been rewarded by his appointment to one of the Chairs of Surgery in Hong Kong. Two of his associates, Stephen Lim and K. H. Lam were other distinguished guests from the Far East who now hold Professorial chairs.

In addition to visits from individual surgeons, various surgical societies have visited the unit. These have been derived from a very wide variety of sources, from a group of Spanish surgeons from Catalonia under the Presidency of Dr Nogueras, to the surgeons from Ulster under the Presidency of Sir Ian Fraser.

It was particularly enjoyable to be able to welcome and to entertain the surgeons from Barcelona where I had first demonstrated my operation of three-stage oesophagectomy and subsequently had the honour of delivering the Gimbernat Lecture in the presence of Mr E. V. Vines, the British Consul-General (Fig. 23).

To welcome Sir Ian Fraser and my colleagues from Ulster was to recall memories of my days as a medical student and to renew my connection with my old university medical school at Queen's.

---

* Prof. John Wong, Now Professor of Surgery, Queen Mary's Hospital, Hong Kong.
† Prof. G. B. Ong O.B.E., F.R.C.S., Professor of Surgery, Queen Mary's Hospital, Hong Kong.

These visits have been characterized by live operating sessions, as well as the presentation of the usual scientific papers and the holding of seminars. Such visits have been of great mutual interest and have been enjoyed by all the staff and have done much to relieve the sensation of isolation when working away from a teaching centre, and when all local contacts are in the District General Hospital.

18

Surgical Travellers – The Moynihan Club

THERE is one respect in which British surgeons are unique in that in the profession there are various groups of surgeons who have formed themselves into surgical travelling clubs. These societies are highly selective and small and they visit various surgical units in this country and overseas. The advantages of this arrangement are very great as there is a full exchange of information, ideas and techniques in smaller conferences and it is widely recognized that this has been a most valuable contribution to British surgery. Perhaps the most famous of these clubs is the Moynihan Surgical Club.

The Moynihan Surgical Club was founded by Mr Berkley G. A. Moynihan (later Lord Moynihan) on 24 July 1909. The concept of the formation of this surgical club was kindled when Moynihan himself visited various surgical clinics in Europe and later on entertained many surgeons from Britain and from the United States of America at his clinic in Leeds.

It was Moynihan's wish that the members of the club should be drawn from those who work, not in London, but in the provinces, since he felt that the London influence in surgery was already too predominant. It is, however, appropriate that the motto of the society should be "Without Frontiers" for the club has travelled internationally and has indeed produced a fellowship of élite provincial surgeons. It is the ambition of every British surgeon outside London to become a member of this club.

I had the unusual good fortune to be elected to the Moynihan Club in 1959 which was the year in which the club celebrated its Golden Jubilee. I was surprised and delighted to receive on 27 September 1959, a letter from Professor Norman Hodgson telling me of my election. I was particularly pleased as, with only one exception (Mr E. R. Frizelle of Leicester), all surgeons elected to the club have formerly been from Provincial Teaching Hospitals. I am glad to say that the importance of the District General Hospital has now become more fully recognized, and the present membership of the club includes some surgeons working only in these district hospitals.

My first attendance was at a meeting of the club held in Sweden in the spring of 1960. Our first centre was in Stockholm and the second centre for the visit was at Lund, a University town in southern Sweden. We travelled by ship from London (Tilbury) to Stockholm and the journey in an ageing passenger ship was most enjoyable. I met for the first time several surgeons whose names were, to me, legend and I felt honoured to be included in their company.

Stockholm is quite a splendid city with fine buildings, and the bridges and waterways have earned for it the title of The Venice of the North. The hospitals were very modern and enormous in size. The Karolinska Hospital had 2,000 beds with mostly individual accommodation. (Fig. 16). The individual rooms provided much appreciated privacy, but supervision of the patients was not as good as in our old fashioned general (Nightingale) wards in Britain. I was greatly impressed by the general atmosphere and Professor Adams Rae, the surgeon in charge was a great personality who operated in a bow-tie under his operating gown. A former opera singer he retained his interest in music and at our official dinner he broke out into song, much to our delight.

Travel from Stockholm to Lund was by Swedish railways which was a very pleasant experience and very different from the British Railway services provided in England at that time. We travelled in arm chairs in an observation car at the back of the train. This enormously enhanced the scenic view of this land of mountains, rivers and lakes. The quieter university atmosphere of Lund was compensated for by the presentation of very highly intellectual contributions by the local surgeons.

Over the years the Moynihan Club visited very many famous centres in Europe and greatly broadened my mental approach to surgery as well as my outlook in the field of politics and people.

On one occasion while in Holland, Prince Bernhard dropped in quite informally to meet the British surgeons. His friendliness and informality

FIGURE 16. *Karolinska Hospital of 2,000 beds in Stockholm.*

were most impressive and sincere. He was in fact a close friend of Professor Boerema* who was entertaining us at his unit at this time.

There were other occasions when the surgical centres surprised me by their excellence, and on other occasions when there was a feeling of disappointment. I had always pictured Vienna as a very beautiful city sited on the blue waters of the river Danube. I found the city indeed very beautiful, but it was not actually on the Danube. The waters certainly were not blue but dull, muddy and brown.

Vienna had always had a great reputation for operations on the stomach and the father of gastric surgery was considered to be Theodore Bilroth who worked in Vienna. I visited the hospital where he had worked in years gone by, the Allgemeines Krankenhaus, founded in 1693 (Fig. 17). I had suspected that the standard of gastric surgery would have been superb but was sadly disappointed. Even the monument to Bilroth in the hospital grounds was somewhat neglected and defaced by the attention of seagulls (Fig. 18).

On the other hand, some quite wonderful surgery was performed in

---

* Prof. Boerema, Professor of Surgery, University of Amsterdam.

units of much less fame. In Montpellier in 1970 I saw some of the finest arterial surgery that I have ever seen in any part of the world. The name of the surgeon was quite unknown to me and it would appear that fame is sometimes more associated with publicity than with merit.

After each visit overseas, as well as visits to hospitals in Britain, one returned to work with renewed ideas and enthusiasm.

Seeing others at work either encouraged renewed efforts to attain perfection, or gave the reassurance that some aspects of one's work were as good as, or even better than, that being carried out at other centres. The effect of these surgical visits was of immense value and in Britain we are most fortunate to have this institution of the surgical travelling club.

FIGURE 17. *The Allgemeines Krankenhaus, where the most famous gastric surgeon, Theodore Bilroth, worked.*

While travelling with the Moynihan Club to the leading surgical centres of Europe, I did not think for one moment that the club would visit my newly established unit at the Friarage Hospital, but greatly to my pleasure the club decided to visit Northallerton.

The meeting was held in April 1966 and was a joint meeting between Northallerton and Newcastle. The first day was to be spent at the Royal Victoria Infirmary in Newcastle and the second day in the Friarage Hospital in Northallerton.

To take the surgeons from Newcastle to Northallerton by rail a special reserved

FIGURE 18. *Statue of Bilroth in the hospital grounds.*

carriage was arranged and the 7.42 a.m. express from Newcastle to Bristol was to make a special stop at Northallerton.

173

The timing was crucial as there was a very full programme and an operation list was due to start at 9.00 a.m. This consisted of a cholecystectomy with pre-operative X-ray cholangiography using for the first time a completely new image intensifier.

The case was on the table awaiting the arrival of the train due at a quarter to nine. This was to be followed by a removal of part of the stomach (gastrectomy) for duodenal ulcer and a bladder operation (prostatectomy) before coffee which was scheduled for 11.30 a.m.

In order to ensure the smooth running of this arrangement the hospital secretary, Mr Alan Wilson, a former R.A.F. fighter pilot, was meeting the train and escorting the guests to the hospital. At 8.45 a.m. while Alan was standing on the platform with the station-master the Newcastle train approached. It was travelling at high speed and obviously showing no signs of slowing down. An emergency stop signal was put into operation by the station-master but it was too late and the train sped past the platform and the next station was Thirsk.

Realising that something had gone wrong, Mr Alec Innes, the club secretary, decided to pull the communication cord. The train then pulled up having overshot the station by about a mile and therefore had to back up to reach the platform in Northallerton.

It was difficult to understand why things had gone wrong after all the arrangements that had been made, but further investigations showed that while everybody at the railway headquarters in Newcastle and even in London knew that this express has to make a special stop at Northallerton, no one had troubled to tell the train driver!

Though the programme was a little delayed by this mishap there was time to show the surgical developments in this new District General Hospital. In particular several cases of ileo-rectal anastomosis for ulcerative colitis were shown. There were some cases of removal of the pancreas (pancreatectomy) for cancer and four different surgical techniques used for growths at varying levels in the oesophagus.

In addition a film made at the Friarage Hospital entitled "Theatre Procedure and Techniques" was shown which illustrated the great saving of time which could be effected by using twin theatres and two operating teams to deal with very large operating lists. Time and action studies had shown that forty per cent of time could be saved in this way. It is disappointing to observe that use of this efficient management technique is not realized by present day lay managers.

On their return journey to Newcastle the club held their Annual General Meeting in the specially reserved compartment on the train. This unusual procedure enabled the annual dinner to be held in New-castle and on time.

There is no doubt that the activities of surgical clubs have made a major contribution to British surgery. This benefit is shared not only by the visiting club but by the surgical unit that acts as their host. It is considered an honour to be asked to receive a travelling club, and great care is taken in preparing the programme and in the presentation.

Preparation involves a great deal of work, not only by the consultant but also those in surgical training. In preparing their presentation they have the opportunity of self assessment, while after the surgical presen-tation there is much discussion which amounts to peer review.

Much political capital is made of the process of audit in an attempt to get what is called "value for money", but in this very process financial consideration by managers impairs the value of the work done. The best type of audit is peer review.

The visit of the Moynihan Club to a unit is always considered a highlight in the life of a surgical unit, and visits are infrequent. In the Newcastle region many years have passed since the episode when the train failed to stop at Northallerton until this year when the club again visited the Newcastle region (Fig. 19).

In this interval of twenty years much change and advance has taken place, and this recent meeting concentrated its visit on the Freeman Hospital, where advances in cardiac surgery have been dramatic. The new generation of surgeons is likely to make the Freeman Hospital as famous in this present age, in cardiac surgery, as Grey Turner and his colleagues made famous the Royal Victoria Infirmary in general surgery in years gone by.

FIGURE 19. *Moynihan Surgical Club visit to Newcastle-upon-Tyne, 1992.*
Front Row: Mr Miller Bell; the author; Arthur Hargreaves; Prof. R. G. Clark; Peter Dickinson, Peter Lord.
Also included: Mr J. Britton; Mr J. Chamberlain; Mr R. Curry; Mr C. Davidson; Mr T. Davis; Mr F. Dean; Mr J. Doran; Mr J. Fielding; Mr J. Hamer; Prof. J. Hardcastle; Mr M. Lyall; Mr C. Mackay; Mr I. McLaren; Mr I MacLeod; Prof. B. Peeling; Mr C. Russell; Mr J. Temple; Mr M. Thompson; Mr R. Wilson.

19

Travel Broadens the Mind

S URGICAL travelling clubs have proved of great value but there are two other features of professional life that have led to foreign travel and to the further broadening of horizons. These features were the lecture tour and the eponymous lecture. Each lecture tour and each eponymous lecture had its own special characteristics. It is not possible to describe each tour or each lecture in detail but it is better to focus on some specific point of special interest or significance in the tour or at the lectures.

SOUTH AFRICA

While lecturing on cancer of the oesophagus at the Royal College of Surgeons in Edinburgh, I met William Silber, a South African surgeon who had a very special interest in cancer of the oesophagus. He asked me if I would take part in a special international conference on oeso-phageal cancer that was to be held the following year in Cape Town. As I was travelling a long way from England to attend the conference he asked me if I would also speak in the hospitals in Johannesburg and in Durban before giving my lectures at the conference in Cape Town. The report of this conference was published in 1978.[27]

It was in South Africa in Johannesburg that I was to learn again that in treating a native population, superstition, and witch-doctoring all play their part. I was aware of the great frequency of cancer of the gullet in the Bantu tribesmen of South Africa but it was in another field, that of social behaviour, that I found most of interest on this visit. I had never seen before the results of such personal violence between the various native populations.

On my first ward round in the hospital in Baraquanath near Johannesburg the first twelve patients in the ward were suffering from stab wounds or gunshot wounds. In this ward there was only one case suffering from natural disease. The casualty department also bore witness to the violence of this society, for in this department blood transfusion sets were already assembled for instant use in anticipation of a patient being admitted having been stabbed through the heart.

This type of injury was a daily occurrence and needless to say these transfusions were constantly required. Strangely enough the violence seemed to be between the black tribesmen themselves and not between black and white.

On the political scene the problems were most difficult, and the closer they are examined the bigger the problems. It is not possible for anyone outside this country to express an informed opinion on the introduction of democracy. Experience has shown that, as in other parts of Africa, democracy means one man one vote—once. Thereafter is established a dictatorship often followed by tribal genocide. This may be about to happen at the present time in South Africa.

The second phase of my tour in South Africa was to Durban where I had the pleasure of visiting the unit of Professor Lyn Baker. The atmosphere in Durban was quite different from that in Johannesburg, and the surgical unit was impressive and run like a British hospital. Looking out from the Elengeni Hotel over the breakers of the shark-infested Indian Ocean was a pleasant sight.

There did not appear to be the same racial problems in Durban as there were in Johannesburg.

In spite of the problems in South Africa it was most pleasant to visit. Cape Town, tucked below the famous Table Mountain, is a remarkable city. From time to time a blanket of cloud would roll over the mountain covering it like a tablecloth and drape down the side of the mountain. It was interesting to visit the Groote Schurr Hospital and realize it was in this hospital that Professor Chris Barnard was the first surgeon to transplant a human heart.

At the conference the leading oesophageal surgeons from all over the world made their contribution and I felt honoured to be invited to give my lecture in such distinguished company. After the conference I was invited to the Civic Reception at the Town Hall and was asked to give the farewell speech. In the Town Hall one could detect the lingering influence of former British Rule. To speak in the Great Hall with pictures of the Royal Family gracing the walls made me feel at home while I was responding to the speech of welcome from the Mayor of the city. I was very touched on this great occasion and felt proud to be British.

On my return home I was to learn that in my absence, at a meeting of the Medical Advisory Committee in Darlington, my two surgical colleagues had decided that my offer to continue the oesophageal work in Darlington on an entirely honorary basis should be turned down. By a strange co-incidence this refusal occurred at the very time I was speaking in the Town Hall in Cape Town of the oesophageal work done in Darlington.

It is sad to think that all the work at Darlington and its international prestige should have been disregarded and the opportunity of Darlington Memorial Hospital becoming a centre of excellence for oesophageal surgery was thrown away.

CANADA

Shortly after the turn of the century my mother's eldest brother was appointed the chief sanitary engineer of Alberta and emigrated to Edmonton.

I had heard much of my Uncle Robert and he was my mother's favourite brother. Perhaps for this reason I had a strong desire to visit Canada, but did not have the opportunity until I met Professor Macbeth. He was so interested in the surgical techniques which I had developed in Darlington and Northallerton that he approached his surgical colleagues in Canada and they invited me to come to Canada. Accordingly, in due course he arranged for a lecture tour of Canada to include Edmonton, Calgary, Vancouver and Sasketchewan. This was indeed a most fascinating and extensive lecture tour lasting for over one month.

The flight to Vancouver was my first crossing of the Atlantic and was uneventful and comfortable. I was deeply impressed to fly up towards the North Pole and to look down on the barren wastes of Labrador and to realize that such vast tracts of cruel and uninhabited land existed in this world.

We staged at Toronto where the Customs officer insisted on looking at my lecture slides. He felt that they contained some secret information, but when he reviewed them he became pale as he saw pictures of a cancer of the gullet being removed at operation. These slides indeed would have deterred the bravest of Customs officers.

We continued our journey to Vancouver and then on to Victoria in Vancouver Island. I was met by Bert Owens, one of my Canadian cousins, who lived in a log cabin on the shores of a small lake where he indulged in his hobby of pigeon racing in which he became a leading personality. I could never have imagined a pigeon costing nearly £1,000 but most of his pigeons were of this value.

As my cousin Bert was showing me round Vancouver Island we encountered a rather exuberant person near the quayside in Victoria who was speaking loudly in a cockney accent. Bert was interested in this strange accent and asked me about it. I explained that a cockney was a Londoner who was born within the sounds of the great Bells of Bow and has a peculiar way of speaking.

I got into conversation with this cockney and asked him how he came to be in Vancouver Island. He explained that he lived in the East End of London for many years and it was his custom every Sunday morning to go out for a drink at the local pub called The Sun and Doves. This he did for many years which enabled him to meet his friends and fellow Londoners. After the war when he was discharged from army service he returned home and to his former habits, but on visiting his favourite pub he found that things were changed.

No longer were the clients in the pub exclusively cockney but people of many races and colours. He described them collectively as "Pakistanians" and was greatly upset that the sanctity of his pub had been eroded by "foreign" people and customs so he left London never to return.

Victoria is a very British looking city and very pro-English. I felt very much at home in this atmosphere and later on when I was offered an extremely attractive post I was indeed tempted to stay.

The Professor of Surgery was Kim Harrison, an extremely handsome and progressive teacher. He showed me round the hospitals which were enormous in size compared with most British hospitals.

I gave some lectures, dealing with cancer of the gullet, peptic ulcer and ulcerative colitis. While I was lecturing I saw in the audience an old friend of mine, Clayton Robinson, who worked with me in London in the Hammersmith Hospital. There were also many surgeons who had emigrated and who were living evidence of the brain drain from Britain. It was good to meet old friends on my first visit to Canada.

In discussions at the hospital I was surprised to find that operating theatres were not worked under the team system. Cases were simply booked in for the operating theatre and the sister on duty took the case. The system is detested by the surgeons in Canada and I was asked to talk to all the staff on the operating team system. This talk was greeted with great approval and, I felt, made a great impression. I was able to show them for the first time the film made at the Friarage Hospital on "Theatre Procedures and Techniques" which emphasized the points that has been raised. It was only in the Cardio-Thoracic Unit under the direction of Clayton Robinson a proper team system was in operation.

The flight from Vancouver to Edmonton was a splendid experience as the weather was perfect. I was greatly impressed by the vastness of the snow covered peaks of the Rockies with its rivers and green-blue lakes. The whole scene was more vast than that of the Alpine peaks over which I had flown so often.

A great group of people were waiting for the plane in Edmonton. We were met by Professor Macbeth and by a cousin whom I had never previously met, but whom my wife recognized , even in the crowd, by a family resemblance. It was a heart warming experience to meet Bob and Monique McBeth and my Canadian cousins.

I was greatly impressed with the hospital and the research facilities in Professor Macbeth's Unit, and only wished that I could have had such help and facilities in my own research efforts in London and in Darlington. It was here that I met the President of the American College of Surgeons, Professor Walter McKenzie who was an international figure in surgery. It was a great pleasure to meet Tom Williams from Liverpool who had just taken over the chair in surgery in Edmonton. I had the privilege of recording the work that had been done in Darlington and which had been seen first hand by Professor Macbeth during his visit to my unit.

The final day in Edmonton was spent with Dr G. W. Scott in the

Charles Council Hospital. This hospital was set aside to serve the peoples of the North West Territories, and it was here that I first met the Eskimo people. They are an unusual and interesting people who live in wild and arid country and speak strange languages and have diseases that seem to be peculiar to their race.

It was in Edmonton, too, that I first had the experience of the nurse who is called a graduate of nursing. I was not at all impressed by the concept or the usefulness of the graduate nurse. They appeared to be neither doctor nor nurse and were in a sort of limbo, being apart from the doctors and yet not doing real nursing.

Each Canadian doctor who had experienced the British scene longed to have proper British nurses rather than those of this American pattern. Yet in Britain today it is sad to relate that there is a tendency to move to the American concept of the graduate nurse.

My journey from Edmonton to Calgary was by car and the scenery was most impressive with its mountains, its rivers and its lakes. The Foothills Hospital was the focus of my visit and we were entertained so well by Professor Tait McPhedren and by his colleagues. The city was different from what I had expected and it turned out to be a city of high rise flats and the only excitement was the Stampede Stadium, which reflected its past history.

In Saskatoon we were met by Professor Ingles and had a most interesting series of surgical discussions. A feature that caused great interest was the second showing of the film on "Theatre Procedures and Techniques". As already mentioned this film illustrated the ideal staffing and running of an operating theatre as a co-ordinated team effort and was quite the reverse of the procedures that I had seen in Canada. The film was attended by a host of nurses and surgeons and again caused a great stir. I felt that it convinced the audience that the team system really does work.

Each centre I visited had its special clinical interest and it was a new experience to see the influence of private medicine in the hospital service. At this time I did not realize that a similar situation with private practice was to arise here in Britain over two decades later.

Returning home we staged again in Toronto and had the unexpected good fortune while walking in the city to see the Queen Mother pass by in an open landau on her way to a church ceremony. In spite of the tight security we got some good photographs of Her Majesty. The other point of interest was a visit to Niagara Falls which is a wonderful sight and which we viewed with the necessary protective oilskin waterproofs. In Canada there was every type of scenery, mountains and plains, rivers and lakes and the distances were very great. There was a great contrast to Britain where all types of scenery can be encountered in a single short journey, but in Canada all journeys were long.

There was some degree of boredom in the vast wheat-lands of Alberta but the mountains, rivers and lakes of the Rockies were really impressive. Bamff and the lovely Lake Louise lived up to the reputations for scenic beauty. Calgary had some lingering atmosphere of cowboys and the Wild West, but Saskatoon had an atmosphere of quiet as it lay in the vast bend of the South Saskatchewan river. In visiting and lecturing in the hospitals in these four great cities, the professional outlook of the doctors was somewhere midway between the quiet British professional outlook and the brash commercial outlook encountered in the United States.

Some years later I had the privilege of a second visit to Canada with the Moynihan Club. On this occasion we concentrated on the surgical centres in Toronto and the eastern side of Canada ending our visit at Halifax in Nova Scotia. *En route* we visited some of the eastern states of the United States of America where the early English settlers came to Virginia in 1607 and thirteen years later where the Pilgrim Fathers landed from the *Mayflower* in Plymouth, Massachusetts. What a pity that English insistence on imposing taxation without representation caused the War of Independence and the sequestration of these English speaking people into two separate nations.

UNITED STATES OF AMERICA

Following the Second World War Britain was exhausted and impoverished and many doctors looked to America for opportunities for experience and for research. As time went on a visit or a period of duty in America became a status symbol or even a qualification. In cynical humour the suffix B. T. A. (been to America) could be added to the British qualification for a candidate seeking a consultant appointment.

My first invitation to America was to a conference on oesophageal surgery in Chicago and my talk was to be on oesophageal cancer. In addition to the lecture I was invited to show some of the films of the operation which I had developed in Darlington. But this visit to the U.S.A. was not one of which all the moments were pleasant.

To make sure that all would go smoothly my wife and I stayed overnight in London and the plane was due to leave Heathrow for Chicago the following morning. Most unfortunately it was at a time when the timetables had just been changed and although we had checked in at terminal three, four hours before the time of take-off a mistake had been made and the plane was really due to take off two hours before the time which we had been given.

As the result of this we missed the plane so that our luggage containing the precious films and my lecture slides, were on the way to Chicago at a time when we were still agitating in the waiting lounge at Heathrow.

British Airways were most upset by the mistake and took every effort to make amends. They fixed us on a special flight to Boston and New York, with a connection to Chicago. As we were crossing the Atlantic I could imagine my luggage going round and round on the turntable in Chicago while the British Airways staff were unable to locate the exact bags.

In the event all went well and miraculously our luggage was located and held safely until we arrived at Chicago. It was then that I realized that luggage could be got onto a plane and the plane proceed without the accompanying passengers. This is a situation which could be exploited by terrorists as did in fact happen in the Lockerbie air disaster some years later, and the aftermath of this disaster lingers on.

The films of oesophagectomy (removal of the gullet) seemed to be well received, but my lecture was messed up by the chairman, a surgeon called David Skinner. The allocation of time for each contributor was misjudged and my lecture had to be cut short so much that my work could not be properly presented. The apology from David Skinner did little or nothing to relieve my frustration and annoyance.

While in Chicago I again met Ronald Belsey, a well known British surgeon from the West Country. He had gone to America after retirement and was continuing an active surgical career. David Skinner had, I believe been his registrar in England and so at least was British trained in surgery if not in chairmanship.

184

Oesophagectomy (removal of the gullet for cancer) is a very major operation requiring special skills and experience. It is an operative procedure usually carried out in old patients who, in other ways, may be quite unfit and therefore the risks are considerable and the mortality rate from operation comparatively high.

While discussing this subject a very well known American surgeon produced mortality figures which were more appropriate to the operations for removal of the gall bladder or the appendix. I was puzzled, if not amazed, at his figures which to me were quite, quite unbelievable. I was to learn that in the American surgical scene, private practice is equated to mortality figures. By excluding the high risk cases the figures can appear, quite unjustifiably, to be very good and private practice proceeds unimpaired.

This is a reminder of the dangers associated with attempts at assessment of performance which is now being introduced into the British medical scene. It is a procedure full of pitfalls and perhaps peer review is the more appropriate method of assessment of merit, as has been the British practice in the allocation of merit awards for the past forty years.

Chicago is a quite remarkable city, situated at the most southern tip of the great Lake Michigan. Subject to high winds, it is known as the Windy City. I had always considered it since boyhood as a city of gangsters with which the name Al Capone was associated but I found this city to be remarkably quiet and well ordered.

It is a city of sky-scrapers and to have dinner in the restaurant at the Sears building with the clouds passing beneath the windows is a remarkable experience. Even when travelling in the lifts it is noted that some lifts do not stop for the first fifty floors while others stop at each floor. The impression given it that of travelling by train where an express stops only at special stations, while the ordinary train stops at every station. The similarity was quite remarkable.

After the conference was over we travelled across America to visit San Francisco. On the way we broke our journey at Las Vegas to enable us to visit the Grand Canyon of which I had heard so much.

Las Vegas is quite a remarkable city. Its lights far exceed those of any other capital and the gaiety and night life were unbelievable. Gambling and stage shows continued throughout the entire twenty-four hours and even the pavements were carpeted outside the restaurants. Las Vegas is a major rail junction and enormously long trains, pulled by as many as four diesel engines passed through the city. At night the wailing of the sirens produced an eerie feeling, while the last truck of the train had a flashing light to let the train driver know that he had not shed any of his trucks on the journey.

Travelling from Las Vegas to the Grand Canyon was by small six-seater aircraft flying at a low altitude of about 4,000 feet. The journey is over the Nevada Desert somewhat south of the area where the Americans test their atomic weapons. The journey was quite a short one and within an hour or so we arrived at the Grand Canyon.

This is a most impressive sight where the high rocky desert land is carved by the deep tortuous gorge of the Grand Canyon. The Canyon itself is most impressive and can be viewed by travel by land or indeed by special aircraft.

Our return from the Canyon to Las Vegas was quite an exciting adventure. The six-seater plane on which we were to travel failed to arrive and we were flown up by a special two-seater aeroplane to continue our journey from Las Vegas to San Francisco. I shall never forget walking out onto the airfield at the Grand Canyon which is situated at a height of about 4,000 feet above sea level.

We were greeted by a man well in his sixties whose name was Dick Hepworth. He was smoking continuously and we climbed on the wing to get into the two-seater with a small dicky seat into which Joan was placed. Sitting beside Dick, shoulder to shoulder, he tried to get the aircraft to start. It was very difficult to get the engine going and he explained that this was due to the altitude. I wondered if the engine would not run at the altitude at ground level, what it would do when it was travelling at 4,000 feet.

In the event we took off satisfactorily and I was very interested to see the various instruments and the way the aircraft was flown. It suddenly crossed my mind what if this man, in advancing age, had a coronary attack and died while we were still airborne. The thought was very frightening and I studied most carefully every manoeuvre he did in flying the aircraft. I think I learned more about flying in the next 50 minutes than I did in my entire previous life.

The only thing that worried me was that should he die, how would we navigate the plane. I noticed that in addition to the sophisticated instruments there was a simple gyroscope stuck onto the windscreen rather like those gyroscopes that some drivers put on the dashboard of their cars. I noticed that the gyroscope was set on due west and I decided that if anything went wrong I would just keep flying due west and look over the edge of the aircraft until we saw Las Vegas. After an extremely bumpy flight in completely crystal clear air we arrived safely at Las Vegas.

During the journey Dick told me that he was a fighter pilot in the war in the American First Air Force. He took part in battles over Britain and it was most interesting to hear his story after the war. He continued in business as well as in flying and, on the death of his wife, he decided even in his advancing years to go back on full time duty as a relief pilot. He also informed me that he used to fly Cassius Clay (Mohammed Ali, the boxer) and asked me if I would like to see him. I announced that I would be delighted to do so and when we landed in Las Vegas he took up to a hotel and there I saw Cassius Clay sitting in the lounge. He was a beautifully built athlete but much smaller in size than I had imagined. He sat there gazing out impassively and to my mind seemed to be punch drunk.

It was a great change to travel by airliner to San Francisco. This was a most attractive city with its hilly aspects and famous cable cars, its famous Fishermen's Wharf, and, out in the bay, the formal Federal Prison of Alcatraz. There was something quite British about the inhabitants of San Francisco that I had not encountered in other cities in the United States.

In such a short visit to the U.S.A. it is not possible to take in the whole scene. My impressions were of the vastness of the country, its youthful or perhaps immature outlook, its worship of strength and its commercial propensities. In surgical work the good seems to be very good indeed while the bad is indeed very bad. It is perhaps true to say that the average is perhaps inferior to the standards that I had been used to in England. In material terms I felt that the profession were much better off than in Britain and more commercially orientated.

HONG KONG/CHINA

The peoples of the Far East, their customs and their culture, hold a great and almost mystical fascination for many people in the West. It was with much surprise and delight that I received in 1977 an invitation to give the Digby Memorial Lecture at the University of Hong Kong. The invitation came from Professor G. B. Ong who was a surgeon with a legendary reputation throughout the world.

My only experience of Eastern customs was that of using chopsticks, a skill I acquired when I was the guest of three outstanding young surgeons from the Far East as mentioned previously who came to visit my unit in Darlington. These were Professor John Wong, Professor K. H. Lam both of Hong Kong and Professor Lim who ultimately became Professor of Surgery at Singapore. After their Darlington visit I rejoined them in London some weeks later and I had instructions in the use of chopsticks in a strictly Chinese Restaurant. It is not difficult for a surgeon to acquire this Eastern skill.

On the advice of these former Far Eastern guests the journey to Hong Kong by Singapore Airlines was a most happy experience of in-flight service and the interest of an overnight stay in Singapore.

To land at the Hong Kong airport is a triumph of modern technology. The approach, in low cloud, through hills and high-rise sky-scrapers, leading to a short runway just next to the sea, is an experience for even the most optimistic and experienced traveller. As a person who, on two occasions, had resolved never to fly again it was a disturbing reminder of what could happen.

The whole atmosphere in Hong Kong was one of work, prosperity and neon signs. The Mandarin Hotel was superb and far more reasonably priced than many third rate hotels in London. Trading was intense and a tailor would happily come to your hotel to make you a suit with two fittings within a span of twenty-four hours and at a third of the price in England.

In spite of the great prosperity there were, however, areas of poverty. In the very many islands that constitute this colony I saw the shacks established by the refugees who had faced many hazards crossing the South China Sea in their escape from Vietnam. It was ten years later that this problem was to be more generally recognized and these refugees are now referred to as the Vietnamese Boat People.

Professor Ong was the senior surgeon at the Queen Mary Hospital and was a prodigious worker. He seemed to attract the most difficult cases, especially those suffering from cancer and his operative surgery was heroic. In the operating theatre he was quite ruthless in obtaining the best out of his staff, but in a social context he was gentle, shy and retiring.

He entertained Joan and me throughout our stay and it was a wonderful experience to have a truly Chinese dinner on a magnificent floating restaurant. We reached the restaurant by crossing the harbour in a sampan, a peculiar Chinese craft on which the boatman and his family and their dog seemed to live. It is interesting to contemplate that the boatman's entire life was spent in the confines of his craft where he was born and on which he will probably die. At the floating restaurant my previous practise in London with chopsticks came in most useful in dealing with a truly Chinese meal.

Ten years later I had the privilege to revisit Hong Kong with the Moynihan Club, when Professor John Wong and Professor K. H. Lam had taken over from Professor Ong and were joint Professors of Surgery. On this particular visit I was interested to note that the techniques for removal of cancer of the oesophagus, developed and demonstrated to our Chinese visitors in Darlington, had been almost universally adopted in the three hospitals that were visited.

This second visit was combined with a short tour in China in which we were joined by two of our friends from the Moynihan Club. Colin Davidson[*] and Philip Lythgoe[†] and their wives formed the party with another American couple. We set out from Hong Kong in the most drab old Boeing 707 that I have ever seen, and even the uniforms of the air hostesses were uninspired in colour and style. The journey to Peking was smooth and on the long, slow descent to the city we were able to see the northern China countryside. It was apparent that there were very few tarmac roads and land travel was over cart tracks. The villages round Peking were primitive indeed. After landing it took two hours for the passengers of this single flight to pass through the red tape of immigration formalities before embarking in an old bus that was to take us to our state run hotel.

---

[*] Colin Davidson, M.Ch., F.R.C.S., Senior Surgeon, Frenchay Hospital. Bristol.
[†] Philip Lythgoe, M.A, F.R.C.S., Senior Surgeon, Royal Infirmary, Preston.

The journey through the back streets of Peking was depressing, the housing appalling and the poverty of the people was extreme.

Our hotel of high tourist grading was reached after dark. The hall was dimly lit and there were queues at the reception with some guests sleeping on sofas due to shortage of space. On attempting to fill in the registration forms we were asked to give our names in Chinese. This added to the depression and gloom that pervaded the whole of the scene. But I noticed that at last Colin Davidson began to smoke his pipe and to smile.

He had decided to write his own version of his name in Chinese and this was indeed an amusing and artistic effort. We all suddenly felt better when we saw his symbol of a kilted Scotsman smoking his pipe under a bamboo roof, and each of us constructed in pseudo-symbols our own individual names. At last we could all laugh.

Our room, described as a double with *en suite* facilities, had the grimmest bathroom I had ever seen. The enamelled bath was old and chipped and black, and there was either hot water, cold water or no water at all. The following morning as I opened the shuttered windows and looked out on the main street the appearance was quite unbelievable. Thousands of people in drab blue-grey denims were cycling to work or crammed into overcrowded trams. There was hardly a single car in sight.

Nearby there were huge cycle parks in which thousands of cycles were stacked and I noticed later that none of these seemed to have any security locks whatever. Stealing in China invokes very severe punishment and theft is very rare.

We visited the silk and carpet factories and saw the Chinese diligently at work during their eight hour day and six day week, at a salary equivalent of £5 per week. I was particularly impressed with the women working in the silk factory where with a surgeon's skill and precision they assembled the fibres of silk strands onto machines. The work in the carpet factory was also impressive and it was interesting to contemplate that these slave workers were producing carpets which would sell in London for thousands of pounds.

In talking to the workers we could detect a feeling of unrest, and they were eager and interested to know of the habits and customs of western peoples. One felt that change might be on the way and the people were becoming dissatisfied with the way things were run in China.

In Peking we visited all the sites of interest and especially the walled cities one of which contains the Forbidden City. The vast Tiananmen Square in Peking was flanked by communist inspired buildings which was a facade and concealed the poverty just outside the square. It seemed sad that some short time after our visit this square should be the scene of the infamous massacre of students mown down by machine-gun fire because of their protest against the oppression of their political masters. (Fig. 20)

Our visit to the great wall of China was most impressive. This 2,000 year old wall stretches for a distance of 2,500 miles and in days gone by served to protect China from incursions of invaders from the north. Looking out from the wall one could contemplate the vastness of Mongolia, the barren mountains of Tibet and the Himalayas rightly regarded as the roof of the world.

A cold, dry wind blowing down from the mountains reduced the

FIGURE 20. *Tiananmen Square – the site of the Chinese massacre of students of recent date.*

temperature to minus twenty degrees and produced frost bite in the unprotected nose and ears. It was at the great wall that I first saw that strange Tibetan ox called a yak, which I had seen in my school books in geography.

Hangchow was our next centre and it was a city of gardens and frozen lakes, and the whole appearance was that of the "willow pattern" on traditional Chinese crockery.

From Hangchow we journeyed by railway to Shanghai which provided us with the opportunity of seeing peasants tilling the land with the implements of centuries past.

Shanghai was a city of much greater prosperity and in which the benefits of former British occupation still lingered. We had lunch in a restaurant with four floors, the bottom floor was abysmal but in ascending order the class of service and amenities increased. Lunch was taken on the top floor and the food and service were acceptable. Similarly, on a river boat trip on the Yangtze Kiang there were five different classes of travel, the best accommodation was called Soft Class. It was strange to note that in the uniformity of a Communist state there are so many different classes of travel and of restaurants. The river is huge and contained many warships emblazoned with the star of Communist China or of merchant ships with the hammer and sickle painted on the funnels.

After the poverty of China it seemed almost indecent to return to the opulence and luxury of Hong Kong. The ordinary Chinese in the mainland seems largely unaware of the success of the industry in Hong Kong, but there is in Hong Kong fear that the transfer to Chinese rule will result in the loss of the opulence they have worked so hard and achieved so successfully under British rule.

IRAN AND SAUDI ARABIA

Though many invitations were received to speak at conferences all over the world, because of pressure of work in my District General Hospitals, most of these invitations had to be refused. In what spare time as was available it was necessary to choose a meeting that might prove of special interest. Invitations to Iran and to Saudi Arabia provided just such opportunities. The invitation to speak in an international conference in the Taj Pahlavi Cancer Institute in Tehran was accepted because it is known that cancer of the gullet is especially common in north east Iran, while the invitation to Riyadh was also accepted because cancer of the gullet in Saudi Arabia is so uncommon. It was of interest to study the causes of this difference in the incidence in this disease.

Tehran, the capital of Iran, is a large city of traffic chaos but the university supported and encouraged by the Shah was well run. At the conference the special features of the lifestyle of the population in the Gombad district of the Caspian litoral was fully discussed in so far as it might reveal opium smoking as one of the causes of cancer of the oesophagus. My contribution was however, in the operative treatment of the condition rather than in its cause.

On the day that I had to give my lecture, I got up early and went down to breakfast in very good time. The service to me was slow and I could not even get my first course. Others came, were served and left while I still waited. I then noted that on the tables of those who were being served there was a pile of money. As the waiter served each course he helped himself to what he thought he should take and so the breakfast service continued with ease. I therefore placed a pile of small change on the table and then at last breakfast was served.

When coming to pay the bill for extras at the end of the conference I was presented with an enormous account. Since I was a guest of the university I had not had any extras and was very surprised to get this big account. Other lecturers from overseas had exactly the same experience. I went therefore to the university to enquire what the position was and was assured that all had already been paid for except for any extras. I spoke to the hotel and they apologized but did not seem to be embarrassed when reminded that some fifteen overseas lecturers were confronted with the same situation.

While in Tehran we had the special interest of seeing the state jewels which were far more extravagant than the crown jewels on display in the Tower of London. We were most impressed by a terrestrial globe with the continents indicated by studded diamonds, sapphires and rubies of infinite value. Also on show were diamonds bigger than the famous Koh-i-noor.

In spite of this national wealth, poverty in Tehran and the surrounding towns was illustrated by the fact that animals shared the same mud dwellings with the Fellahin peasants.

Such cottage industries as were carried out were in the making of carpets, where the whole family including the youngest children took part in the process.

Realizing the industrial weakness of the country and looking to the time when the oil would run out, the Shah was anxious to encourage manufacturing and to include women in the work force. In this he was opposed by the Mullahs who were the religious leaders. In spite of his well equipped army and air force he was soon to be deposed and replaced by the Ayatollah Khomeni.

It was so pleasant after the activity of the conference to have a few days' rest at Esfahan where we stayed in the Shah Abbas Hotel to which the Shah was a frequent visitor. It was a delightful hotel with court yards and minarets and all the atmosphere of the East. We were greeted and looked after by a fascinating little man who was our servant for the stay in this superb hotel (Fig. 21).

In a visit to Riyadh two years later the opulence of Saudi Arabia was apparent, and no expense was spared to look after the guest speakers. The whole of professional society seemed to be more orientated towards the west than in the other Middle East countries visited.

This conference was of general interest and the proceedings have been published in 1980.* After the conference our journey home was interrupted by an unscheduled diversion to Jiddah to pick up a Saudi prince and his great retinue who were accommodated in the upper deck of the Boeing 747. I was told that this prince was the owner of the airline but the staff were most apologetic about the inconvenience caused by the additional stop.

---

* Proceedings of the fifth Saudi Medical Meeting. Published by the University of Riyadh. Ed. Professor Elsheikh Mahgoub

FIGURE 21. *The Shah Abbas Hotel in Esfahan, where the Shah used to take his holidays.*

ARGENTINA

In medical care there is a triad of problems to be dealt with, infections, degenerative diseases and cancer. In the present state of our knowledge infective diseases can be prevented by immunization or successfully treated by antibiotics. Degenerative disease can be treated by joint or organ repair or replacement, but cancer still presents the major problem which is not yet completely solved.

The fact that malignant disease is still the major threat to life has resulted in national and international organizations being formed in the fight against cancer. The most prestigious organization in helping to co-ordinate scientific effort in cancer treatment is the U.I.C.C. (Union Internationale Contra Cancer). This international organization was formed some years ago and has thrived in its constant activity in the study of malignant disease. The society holds international conferences every four years as does its athletic counterpart in the Olympic Games.

In 1976 I was asked if I would report on my work on oesophageal cancer at the twelfth International Conference to be held in Buenos Aires in October 1978.

I felt that I was being given the opportunity to present an up to date report on the operative techniques which have been developed in Darlington and Northallerton over a period of twenty-five years. I accepted this invitation with enthusiasm but within a month or two I had letters from Amnesty International asking me not to go to the Congress. They considered that the military regime in Argentina had encroached on human rights and that a boycott should be imposed.

After much consultation and a great deal of thought I decided to attend the conference in spite of the warnings from Amnesty International. This society sent me, over the ensuing year, much detail of alleged infringements of human rights and I soon accumulated a dossier of documents all of which I had not time to consider fully. The final request was for me to inquire regarding the whereabouts of over ten missing persons and this I agreed to do.

In due course on 3 October 1978 my wife and I set out on the flight to South America. During the flight I had the time to read more completely the dossier from Amnesty International and suddenly realized that were I to be searched in Argentina I might well be detained for possessing details so critical and damning of the military junta that had seized power. Realizing that discretion was the better part of valour, when we staged at Rio de Janeiro, I left a great pile of documents in the airport lounge and retained only the list of missing persons.

Buenos Aires was quite a pleasant city and over the week-end before the conference I looked around to locate the various conference halls and in particular the place that I was to give my address and the theatre where I was to show my surgical film.

While strolling near the conference hall on Sunday morning I met a couple of visitors. They asked me in a marked Yankee accent if I spoke American. I replied that I did not speak American but that I could speak very good English. The expression on their faces was one of puzzlement which slowly melted into a smile as the penny dropped. They were fellow delegates to the conference.

I had been advised to contact the British Ambassador (or Consul) as soon as possible after my arrival in Argentina and I attempted to do so. Unfortunately, no one in the hotel seemed to know where the Consulate was and I was unable to find it in the telephone book. I rang various embassies without success but at last was given the required address by the Nicaraguan Embassy.

I set out by taxi but the driver said he did not know the address though it was in a well-known street and I had been able to locate it on my map. Under pressure the driver ultimately completed the journey to the address which he pretended not to know and arrived at the embassy. I came to the conclusion that there was a strong anti-British feeling in Argentina which was soon to be expressed by the invasion of the Falkland Islands.

I was greeted most cordially by a Mr Chick and I explained to him my predicament with Amnesty International and he was indeed most helpful. He explained the position of the military regime and how, after years of civil disorder which the police were unable to control, the army were at long last obliged to take over control of the state.

Following the death of Perón and his widow's ineffectual control, the country had been torn by strife, kidnapping and murders which had become daily occurrences. Occasionally great battles would taken place between the police and the various gangs and the death rate was high. The army did indeed restore law and order.

I spoke to many of my surgical colleagues from Argentina and they felt that even with all the disadvantages of the military regime they were much safer. Many surgeons had been under constant fear of kidnap and extortion by various political groups and welcomed the restoration of peace to the city. Any fictitious emergency call might result in kidnap and the victim being held to ransom, a situation which persisted until the army took control.

Inflation in Argentina was rampant and was, I think, at a level of thirty-nine per cent per month; even a cup of tea cost a fortune. It seemed that General Galtieri had an economic disaster on his hands and I formed the opinion that his claim to the Islas Malvinas (Falkland Islands) was an attempt to divert attention from his many domestic problems.

It was about this time that the British withdrew the solitary protecting patrol vessel H.M.S. *Endurance* from the Falklands for repair, and the Falkland War was soon to start. It is difficult to believe that at this stage Britain had any intention of defending the Falklands, but suddenly had a change of heart. Could Margaret Thatcher have caused this change of

FIGURE 22. *The Effigy of Christ towering over the city of Rio de Janeiro and the Copacabana Beach.*

heart? A few more destroyers of the Royal Navy would, I am sure, have prevented this unnecessary war.

The conference itself was truly international and the event was similar in size to that of the Football World Cup. There were hundreds of delegates from the United States, from Canada and Japan, and a substantial number from Europe but only a handful from Britain. It may well be that Amnesty International's appeal for a boycott had its effect. It was however very encouraging to have an old friend of mine, Ronald

Raven* a great cancer specialist sitting in the front seat as I delivered my address.

The delegates were very well looked after and very well entertained. General Galtieri held a reception when we all met him and then there was a barbecue of unprecedented size. The police produced an acrobatic horse show of outstanding skill.

The final entertainment was a cattle round up where the gauchos produced a stampede which was indeed most impressive. These highly skilled horsemen or cowboys could work a huge herd of cattle into a frenzy and have them racing purposelessly across the prairie covered by a cloud of sweat until sheer exhaustion depleted their number and the stampede petered out.

On the way home we stayed at Rio de Janiero with its unforgettable bay and Sugar Loaf Mountain. An effigy of Christ towers beneficently from one of the high hills that overlooks the city and the copacabana beach. (Fig. 22). While hang gliders hovered over the city the urchins in the town were stealing food from the very plates in the restaurants as you tried to have a meal. It was a mixture of grandeur and poverty. If effigies could speak I wonder what this great effigy would say of what was happening in the fantastic city at its feet.

The proceedings of this conference were published by Pergamon Press[28] of which the now notorious Robert Maxwell was the chairman. At the beginning of the conference orders were taken for the purchase of the several volumes recording the various papers presented by authors from all over the world. I noted the original price of the volumes was reduced as the conference drew to its close, perhaps because the books were not selling as well as expected.

In submitting my chapter my secretary was most puzzled in having to type on very special paper, and was not allowed to make any erasures or corrections. The reason for these special precautions was soon to become clear. When volume 9 was published it was apparent that each paper was reproduced by photostat so that the type of script from an author from Japan or one from Chile varied enormously in appearance. This was in marked contrast to a normal surgical textbook where each

---

* Ronald W. Raven O.B.E., T.D., F.R.C.S., Hon. Consultant Surgeon, Royal Marsden Hospital, and Westminster Hospital, London

contribution is reset and printed with characters of appropriate type to produce a text which is wholly compatible. The publication by Pergamon Press was more an exercise in book binding rather than in publication, and no doubt cost much less to produce, and resulted in higher profits.

SPAIN

After the war Spain assumed the image of a huge resort where sun and sand combined to produce the cheapest holidays obtainable in all Europe. Having enjoyed the Spanish beaches for some years after the war, Spain for me took on a very different image. With increasing contributions in the surgical journals on the treatment of cancer of the oesophagus, many invitations were received from all parts of Europe to go and lecture on this special subject.

There was, however, one invitation which was quite different and that came from Spain. Dr Curto-Cardus wrote to me inviting me to come and operate in a very unusual and lovely new hospital which had just been built in Barcelona.* This was the first invitation to operate abroad and it was accepted with a mixture of expectation and apprehension. Expectation at the opportunity of demonstrating to the Spanish surgeons a completely new technique, but apprehension at the prospect of working with a completely strange team who had never done the procedure before and who did not even speak English.

I was met at the airport by Dr Curto-Cardus and by his assistant Dr Cabre who had spent some considerable time in England. The case was a man with a cancer of the middle of the gullet. The operation consisted of three separate procedures which was designed to take out the growth and the entire gullet and to replace it with the stomach which was brought up into the neck. Between each stage there was the now traditional cup of tea to provide a useful stimulus and intermission. It was the operation that I first performed in the Friarage Hospital in Northallerton in 1962.

The hospital Principes de Espana was a completely new hospital of revolutionary design. In planning the hospital several of the medical staff travelled to various parts of the world to inspect different hospitals. It

---

* Residencia Sanitaria de la Seguridad Social, Principes de Espana

was in Israel where they saw a hospital which made the most favourable impression, and the architects of this hospital were asked to design the new hospital in Barcelona.

The general appearance was most unusual and impressive. It consisted of three circular buildings rather like huge chimneys but of different sizes. Each surgical unit had a central station, surrounding which were separate wards radiating out like the spokes of a great wheel. The advantage of this design was that the nurses at the central station had monitors related to each ward and could have direct vision of every patient. The walking distance to patients was therefore short which avoided staff fatigue and each patient had privacy but was under constant observation.

The operating theatre was overcrowded with surgeons from all over Spain. There were two interpreters, one to convey my requests to the theatre staff and the second to explain to the surgeons all the details of the operative techniques that were being carried out. At times the atmosphere was that of the Tower of Babel with excited surgeons anxious to ask questions all at the same time.

There was certainly great interest and excitement and the operation proceeded very satisfactorily. Between each stage I was served as already noted with tea and biscuits served on a silver tray by a waiter with a bow tie under his theatre gown. What a change from Darlington and Northallerton. When I returned that night to the Hotel Diplomatique I was tired out but happy to have made so many friends among my Spanish colleagues.

Some years later I was very honoured to be awarded the Gimbernat Prize in Barcelona and to be elected an honorary member to the staff of the Hospital de la Santa Cruz and San Pablo. Gimbernat, born in 1734, the son of a Catalonian farm worker, was to become an anatomist surgeon of outstanding merit and the greatest surgeon of his day. He became adviser to the Spanish Court and had the confidence of three successive Spanish Kings. It was to commemorate his work that the Prize was established and the Gimbernat Medal awarded to "an outstanding internationally known surgeon".

The lecture was delivered in the very theatre where this famous Spanish surgeon/anatomist used to work. The lectern was placed on the anatomy table and one could picture this great man dissecting out the

FIGURE 23. *Dinner with the British Consul in Barcelona after delivering the Gimbernat Lecture.*

tissues of the groin, and describing the band of fibrous tissue which was to be described as Gimbernat's ligament, and his name was to enter posterity. The atmosphere was most touching and I was particularly delighted that H.M. British Consul-General, E. V. Vines was present at the lecture and at the dinner which followed that evening under the Presidency of Professor Puig Lacalle, one of Spain's leading surgeons. (Fig. 23)

Some years later when I became President of the Moynihan Club I decided that the club meeting should be in Spain and chose Barcelona and Madrid as the centres for our meeting. Going to Barcelona was like going home but Madrid had an atmosphere that was somewhat different. While at the meeting in Madrid I was asked to operate on another case

FIGURE 24. *Professor Louis Barros (centre) of Madrid at the Moynihan Club visit to Madrid, with the author and his wife and other Spanish surgeons.*

of cancer and it was a very great pleasure to do so in the capital of Spain, at the invitation of Professor Louis Barros. (Fig. 24)

It is perhaps of special interest that our host in Madrid was the senior surgeon, Louis Barros. He was a man of great skill and charm and I was to learn from him the story of General Franco's illness.

It would appear that Franco developed a simple perforated ulcer which in the ordinary course of events required a straightforward operation. Unfortunately, due to a series of events, this condition was not recognized and his progress was very unsatisfactory and his life was in grave danger.

It was most important that, for political reasons, Franco should not die at this particular time. Though apparently peaceable on the surface, Spain at this time was still deeply divided, and the wounds of the civil war had scarcely healed. For this reason it was most important that Franco should survive to retain political stability, so every effort was made to prolong his life even though he was over eighty years of age. After many vicissitudes and a galaxy of life support technique he was able to survive long enough to enable a smooth transfer of power to Juan Carlos, who, with great skill and courage, restored the monarchy to Spain after years of dictatorship.

AUSTRALIA AND NEW ZEALAND

One of the most remarkable features noticed on coming to London for my first appointment as a house surgeon was the number of doctors who had come from Australia and New Zealand. These doctors from "down under" were regarded very much as citizens of the British Empire and were considered as one of us. This tendency continued after the war and in Darlington and Northallerton we had many doctors who came to train in surgery before returning to their own countries.

The first to join the staff of the Friarage was a Dr J. J. Hall from New Zealand. His work was very good and he heralded a whole series of graduates from "down under".

Perhaps the most colourful person was a very tall Australian called Cutler who was six feet eight in height, whose uncle had won the V.C. in the war, and is at present the Governor-General of New South Wales. One of Cutler's other colleagues, Dr David Annetts, was the hardest worker I have ever seen, and another colleague Dr Marriot the best anatomist. Dr Marriot was very interested in comparative anatomy and used to lecture us all on the importance of the koala bear, that special species of tree bear indigenous to Australia.

The most recent visitor was Ian O'Rourke who brought over his entire family from Australia and made quite an impression in Darlington. When I was invited by Sir John Loewenthal to visit Australia it was O'Rourke, with his local knowledge, who arranged the trip and greeted us on our arrival in Sidney.

In actual fact the first part of our trip "down under" was to Auckland in New Zealand. I spent a week with Professor Eric Nansen in the University of Auckland and there was much exchange of ideas as Professor Nansen, who had formerly visited me in Darlington was also interested in oesophageal surgery.

After a few days rest, I visited the hot springs and marvelled at the boiling mud lakes of Rotorua. New Zealand was a most pleasant land and the people were more British than the British, and proud of their ancestry.

Australia was very different in atmosphere and culture and they were anxious to demonstrate their own independence. Sydney was an unusual and very modern city. I lectured at various hospitals in Sydney and a group of former surgical registrars who had been with me in Darlington very kindly gave me a party of special welcome.[*] It was a touching reunion and greatly enjoyed.

Of more recent date while watching the Australian rugby team on television I noted a very tall Australian who was so tall he could easily reach up to the ball in the line outs. A close up showed the unmistakable features of Dr Cutler's son, who I believe was even taller than his father at six feet ten.

Professor Maurice Ewing who was well known to me when we worked together at the Hammersmith Hospital entertained us in Melbourne and I had the great interest to give details of the work of the former Australian E. C. T. Milligan to the Australian College of Surgeons for inclusion in their annals.

Perhaps the most unexpectedly interesting visit was to Newcastle an

---

[*] Ian O'Rourke, David Annetts, David Cutler, Dr Marriot, Chester Troy, Ron Wiles, Philip Wiles et alia.

industrial mining town about 100 miles north of Sydney. I was guest lecturer at the Hunter Surgical Society and was honoured to be presented by the President, Bruce Messmer, with a book, *Dawn of the Valley* and a further book, *Newcastle and the Hunter Valley*. These books gave an account of the early Australian settlers carving their way out of the wilderness of the Hunter River Valley to establish their homes.

I was greatly impressed by the surgeons of Newcastle, especially with John Gilles a young surgeon whom I first met at the Royal College of Surgeons Meeting in Kuala Lumpur. He was a most progressive and up and coming young surgeon.

The visit to Australia and New Zealand was a meeting of old friends and will long be remembered.

On the return journey home we had the rather unusual experience of being the only two passengers in a jumbo jet. This was on the first part of the journey from Melbourne to Sydney. It was strange to be able to wander round in this great plane fully staffed with cabin crew, but with only two passengers. It is even more remarkable that on this short journey our luggage was lost, and had apparently been put on a different plane from Melbourne to Sydney, and when finally located our bags were searched with a thoroughness that I had never experienced before. I could not help but think that the security officers thought there must be something seriously amiss when the luggage of the only two passengers was lost.

EUROPE

Having already visited most of the major centres in Europe I had an overall picture of European surgery, its highlights and its disappointments. I cannot compare European surgery with that in North America, for though I have listened to many lectures from surgeons in the United States and Canada, I have never had the opportunity of seeing them working in the operating theatre which is the real test.

Comparisons of operative mortality rates are often used as a measure of surgical merit. There are, however, fallacies in using this in making comparisons. As already mentioned I had the impression that much of the published work in America was on selected cases where operative mortality could be low, as publishing poor results could affect the private practice on which the incomes of surgeons depend. It would be a pity if the market forces, surgical audit, and statistics with all their fallacies, which have so recently been introduced into the National Health Service in Britain should conceal the truth and affect the true scientific advance on which the future of the patients depend.

There are in Europe many personalities and it has been of great interest to contribute to surgical panels and seminars because under the barrage of questions (as in the House of Commons in Westminster) much truth is revealed. One of the most enjoyable of these sessions was in Paris where I first met Professor Lortat Jacob of whose work I had read a great deal. He was the father figure of French oesophageal surgery rather like Sir Ian Fraser, his counterpart in general surgery in Britain. (Fig. 25).

Surgery is a universal art and science in which nationality and parochialism have no part. To visit colleagues abroad is both interesting and stimulating and I believe of mutual benefit. It is not only in the formal

FIGURE 25. *Conference Panel of European Oesophageal Surgeons in Paris.*

lectures or in public discussions that ideas arise, but often in the informal conversations that take place on these occasions.

One is often reassured that what one is doing is right, while observation of other surgeons' work is conducive to a dynamic approach to the problems that confront the medical profession throughout the world. There is no doubt that the medical profession is a brotherhood that knows no frontiers and one can feel at home in any part of the world while being with medical colleagues.

There is no doubt that travel broadens the mind and increases insight into many problems. It can, however, be a rather lonely occupation in strange and foreign lands. I am glad to say that in all my world-wide travels, except one, I have had the company and support of my wife Joan. It may well be that Joan has seen more of the world than anyone else, except Kate Adie and Mrs Thatcher!

20

The Royal Colleges of Surgeons

THE Royal Colleges of Surgeons have their roots deep in centuries past. The origins of the Royal College of England date back to the reign of Henry VIII (1540), while those of the Edinburgh College go back to the time of the Battle of Flodden. The institution of the colleges was to protect standards of surgical practice and to teach. The first Charter of Incorporation of Barber Surgeons imposed the obligation to teach and the granting of Royal status by George III in 1778 emphasized this solemn duty. Today the attainment of the Fellowship (F.R.C.S.) is essential to all those who wish to practice surgery in Britain.

In the maintenance of standards the University Medical Schools have selected only those of highest potential for admission to the Faculty of Medicine, and the five year university course is the longest and most arduous of all the faculties. It is perhaps because of these features that, of all the learned professions, the doctor commands the greatest respect. It is to be hoped that the effect of joining the European Community will not lower the high standards set for doctors in Great Britain.

In view of the dramatic advances in surgery the maintenance of standards of patient care is ever present in the minds of the council of the surgical colleges. In 1963 the English College introduced a pilot scheme for surgical training by appointing a surgical tutor in certain selected hospitals. Darlington Memorial Hospital was one of those specially selected and the author had the privilege to be one of the first surgical tutors ever appointed.

The idea of establishing a surgical tutor in a District General Hospital, as distinct from a Teaching Hospital, was a recognition of the major surgical work that was now being done in these peripheral hospitals. The experiment was a great success and subsequently surgical tutors were appointed all over the country to provide a solid basis for postgraduate surgical education.

On being appointed Surgical Tutor a training scheme in Darlington was carefully planned and in each term throughout the year a series of lectures were arranged in which surgeons of great distinction came to Darlington to speak to the trainees and to the consultant staff.* The introduction of this scheme for surgical training is an example of the importance of starting a pilot scheme before embarking on any major change and should be adopted in other spheres within and without the health service.

THE HUNTERIAN PROFESSORSHIP

The Royal College of Surgeons of England award to selected surgeons a Hunterian Professorship. This was first instituted in 1805 and each year several professorships are awarded. (Fig. 26) At a colourful ceremony in Lincoln's Inn, the Hunterian Lecture is duly delivered in the Great Hall of the College. The ceremony is quite impressive and the President of the College leads the procession of Council all in their academic robes, while following behind them is the Hunterian Professor who is about to deliver his lecture. (Fig. 27) When duly installed on the rostrum the Professor bows to the President and then gives his address.

It is an elegant and overawing experience and there is a story of an Hunterian Professor who was overcome by the events. While the procession was moving forward to take its place on the rostrum, the professor became so nervous that he suddenly ran away. As he was at the back of the procession his escape was unnoticed so that when the President and Council turned to receive him he was found to be missing.

It was the custom that the lecture was delivered at the Royal College

* 1. Sir John Peel. Surgeon to H.M. The Queen 2. Sir Stanford Cade. Formerly Senior Consultant Surgeon, Westminster Hospital, London. 3. Prof. Ian Aird. London Postgraduate Medical School 4. Prof. P. S. Boulter. President Royal College of Surgeons of Edinburgh 5. Prof. Dennis Melrose. Hammersmith Hospital 6. Mr Harold Edwards. King's College Hospital. 7. Prof. Ralph Shackman. Professor of Urology, Hammersmith Hospital, London et alia

FIGURE 26. *Sir Thomas Holmes Sellors, President of the Royal College of Surgeons of England (right) and the author.*

in London and on occasions the lectures were poorly attended. Sir Thomas Holmes Sellers was always emphasizing the fact that the Royal College was a college for all England and not only for London.

When I was honoured by the Hunterian Professorship in 1972, I suggested that if he really meant what he was saying, could not the lecture be held in Darlington rather than in London. Much to my surprise and delight this was agreed to and for the first time a Hunterian Professor delivered the lecture in a District General Hospital outside London.

Preparation for the lecture which was to be held on the 10 March 1972 was intense as the whole idea was new and there was no precedent. I decided to have a very different approach to that which I had seen in London. As the council were coming all the way from London and were wishing to project their image outside the capital special features were required. Arrangements were made for a stay of two nights.

Unfortunately, the hotel in Darlington which was most suitable to provide accommodation was at this time having major repairs and was unavailable. Due to the kindness of an old friend, "Jim" Roberts and his

FIGURE 27. *Hunterian Professorship in Darlington in 1972.*
(Right to left): Mr Norman Carpenter, C.B.E.; Sir Edward Muir, K.V.C.O., C.B.E.;
Sir Thomas Holmes Sellors; Mr Guy Blackburn, M.B.E.; Sir William Lee (Chairman
of the Newcastle Regional Hospital Board); Mr Alan Brown (Chairman of the Dar-
lington Hospital Management Committee); Professor of Anatomy, Newcastle; Professor
Reginald Hall, Professor of Medicine, Newcaslte-upon-Tyne.

associate Charles Amer reservations were made at the Tall Trees Hotel, a quiet country hotel convenient to Darlington. I was pleased to greet the council on their arrival at Darlington and to escort them to their hotel.

The programme the following day started with lunch at the Darlington Memorial Hospital when the surgeons of the Newcastle Region were invited to meet the President and members of Council. Sir William Lee, the Chairman of the Regional Hospital Board and the Senior Administrative Medical Officer Dr Sackwood joined us to lunch and it was quite a unique occasion.

The scientific programme began after lunch when Dr J. Hampson, the Senior Physician, acted as chairman and introduced my film showing the work developed on oesophageal (gullet) cancer in the previous twenty years in Darlington and in Northallerton.

At tea the general practitioners were invited to meet the Council of the College. I felt that it was most important to emphasize the unity of the profession and to demonstrate the excellent relationship which existed between the general practitioners and the consultants in the hospital in Darlington and in Northallerton.

The procession started after tea and the lecture on cancer of the gullet was delivered to a crowded hall with over 400 in the audience which, I believe, was the biggest attendance ever recorded at an Hunterian Lecture. (Fig. 27). The lecture was a simple record of the start and development of operative treatment for this very special form of cancer. Completely new techniques were described and the results of treatment outlined.

In the evening a special dinner was arranged at the Tall Trees Hotel at which the Marquis and Marchioness of Zetland and Sir William and Lady Lee were the guests of honour (Fig. 28). Included in the guests were representatives of all staff who had helped from the theatre technician to the first assistant.

Darlington has always been known as a "railway town" and the first

FIGURE 28. *Banquet after the Hunterian Lecture.*
(Left to right): The Marquis of Zetland; Joan McKeown; the author; The Marchioness of Zetland; Sir Thomas Holmes Sellors; Lady Sellors; Lady Lee and Sir William Lee.

steam train hauled by *Locomotion No 1* ran on the Darlington and Stockton Railway. The stationmaster at Darlington was a patient of mine and I mentioned that we were having a very special visit from the Royal College of Surgeons and thought that they might be interested in the railway history. He immediately suggested that they should have the staff present to show the Members of the Council the intricacies of the early steam locomotive and one of its successors *The Derwent* which were proudly on show on the railway platform. The morning after the lecture the President and Council assembled on the platform on one of the clearest and coldest spring days that I ever remember. It was fascinating to see Sir Thomas Holmes Sellors* and Sir Edward Muir† climbing over this ancient locomotive while we were all instructed on its mechanisms by railway staff in smart uniforms and peaked caps. After an hour the Secretary of the College, Mr Johnson-Gilbert, looking blue with cold, escorted the Council into the special reserved carriage that was to take them on their return journey to London.

No such function can be arranged without a great deal of help from many sources. My secretary, Eileen Raine, made all the arrangements for the visit and Mr George Beckwith, the Hospital Secretary arranged for lunch and tea at the hospital.

The interest and support of local businessmen was quite remarkable. When I came to pay the bill for the banquet it was already paid and when the Secretary of the College came to pay the hotel bill for the accommodation of the College Council it, too, had been settled. The generosity and interest of the people of Darlington was a heart warming experience I am very grateful for all their support. I would especially like to thank Canon Leonard Piper, the vicar of Hurworth, and his wife Millie for their great help with the social aspects of this visit.

This Hunterian Lecture was to set a precedent and since that time in 1972 many Hunterian Professors have delivered their lectures outside London either in the Teaching or in the District General Hospitals. It is with pride that Darlington can say it was the first.

---

* Sir Thomas Holmes Sellors, President of the Royal College of Surgeons of England.
† Sir Edward Muir, Surgeon to H.M. The Queen.

EDINBURGH COLLEGE LECTURER

The Edinburgh College have always been aware of the importance of holding meetings and having lectures "out with Edinburgh". Each year they award a Lectureship in which the lecturer gives his address at the university at which he qualified, rather than at the hospital at which he works.

In 1976 I had the great honour of being awarded the third Annual College Lectureship which meant returning to Belfast to my undergraduate Teaching Hospital to give this lecture and this seemed strange after an interval of so many years. I was particularly pleased to give this lecture and to know that my two predecessors were Professor C. C. Clarke of Aberdeen and Sir Douglas Black of London.

It was indeed a strange feeling to be invited to give this prestigious lecture, not at the invitation of my Medical School or the Queen's University, but at the invitation of the Royal College of Surgeons of Edinburgh.

In choosing the subject of the lecture I felt that the influence of the work being done at the District General Hospitals throughout the country was becoming so important that the lecture was entitled "The Surgery of a District General Hospital". As a tribute to the staff of Darlington Memorial Hospital who had so loyally supported me for so many years, my theatre sister* and my secretary† accompanied Joan and me on our car journey to Ulster.

It was the year 1976, at a time when terrorism in Ulster was rife in this strife torn Province. Arrangements were made for the Council Members to receive private hospitality as to stay in hotels was considered unsafe.

Sir Ian and Lady Fraser kindly invited us to stay at their home in Upper Malone Road which was indeed most welcome in view of the I.R.A. campaign of terror. I remember walking up the drive to his home and remarking that the windows of the house seemed a little unusual. On entering the hall there were laminated plastic bullet proof screens

---

* 1. Sister Hilary Atkinson—Theatre Sister
† 2. Eileen Raine—Medical Secretary

and the rather peculiar windows enabled those inside to see out without allowing those outside to see in.

It was then that I realized that because of the great respect in which Sir Ian was held by all sections of the population, he had been made chairman of the Police Authority, but it was felt that precautions were necessary for his protection. The necessity of this protection was emphasized by the fact that a house closely adjacent to his home had been set on fire two days previously in the mistaken belief that it was his home.

The lecture proceeded with the usual formality and I told of the establishment of a consultant service for the first time in Darlington and Northallerton. I reported on the work on peptic ulcer, on ulcerative colitis and of the new operations for cancer of the gullet. As I delivered the lecture I wondered what would have happened had I stayed on in Belfast and whether I would have been able to do this work in my own Medical School. On reflection perhaps it was better to move to "fresh woods and pastures new".

The morning after the official College Dinner, Sir Ian took me in his car and I saw the scenes of my student days. The road names are now household words in the catalogue of sectarian violence. The Falls, The Grosvenor and the Shankhill Roads and the Ardoyne districts are all too familiar names in this record of killing.

The speed reducing mounds (sleeping policemen) were on all the streets, and many of the gables of disused houses were painted in colours and pseudo-heraldry to proclaim support for the I.R.A. or some other para-military organization. As we passed from one street to another I felt that at any time snipers might open fire but Sir Ian drove on without a care in the world and as we passed by he gave occasional signs of recognition to some of his former patients.

In contemplation it is sad to see this Province torn asunder by the divisiveness of organized religion, a state of affairs that seems to arise in Bosnia and so many other parts of the world today. The most extraordinary feature in Ulster is that the ordinary citizen gets on with his work and is able to carry on in spite of bombs and bullets. The ordinary people of Ulster deserve an award just as the people of Malta were rewarded for steadfastness during the war and the island became known as the George Cross Island. Perhaps the citizens of Northern Ireland should be awarded the "Ulster Cross".

THE MCKEOWN MEDAL

At the College Lecture in Belfast it was suggested by Sir Ian Fraser that it would have been appropriate to award a medal to commemorate the occasion. I considered this idea and was much impressed by this concept. Some year or two later I suggested to the President of the Edinburgh College, Mr James A. Ross, M.B.E., that I would be happy to donate to the College a medal to be awarded each year to the College Lecturer. This suggestion was well received and the first medal (Fig. 29) was awarded to Professor Dennis N. Walder who delivered his lecture in Newcastle on the 23 March 1979. Since then twelve medals have been awarded to a most impressive list of distinguished surgeons.

Professor D. N. Walder	Newcastle upon Tyne	1979
Professor I. S. Smillie, O.B.E.,	Perth	1980
Professor I. D. A. Johnston	Belfast	1981
Professor D. C. Carter	Carlisle	1982
Professor George Murdoch	Falkirk	1983
Sir Patrick Forrest	Dundee	1984
Mr N. A. Matheson	Aberdeen	1985
Mr Peter Edmond C.B.E.	Inverness	1986

FIGURE 29. *The Royal College of Surgeons of Edinburgh Lecture – The McKeown Medal.*

Miss Carys M. Bannister	Manchester	1987
Mr R. Myles Gibson	Scarborough	1988
Mr R. M. R. Taylor	Newcastle-upon-Tyne	1989
Mr J. H. Steyn	Aberdeen	1991
Mr S. J. Leinster	Liverpool	1992
Mr K. D. Boffard	Belfast	1993

21

The London Medical Scene

EACH morning precisely at 7 a.m. I am awakened by the sound of an aircraft passing over my home. It is the British Midland flight from Teesside to London Heathrow. This serves as a daily reminder of the busiest period of what was for me an already very busy life.

At a time when my clinical work was at its peak, I was asked by the Minister of State to serve on several important committees including the Central Health Services Council and the Central Council for Postgraduate Education.

At this time too I was appointed to the Specialist Advisory Committee (S.A.C.) to advise the Royal Colleges on the surgical training programmes being set up throughout the country. I was also appointed to the Regional Training Committee to advise on the implementation of these programmes in the Newcastle-upon-Tyne region. To these commitments must be added the membership of the Board of Science of the British Medical Association.

These committees covered virtually all aspects of medicine and of the National Health Service. Though my work load at this time was enormous I felt that with the experience gained in working in a busy District General Hospital one could make a contribution from the peripheral ground roots of clinical medicine to the general central direction of the National Health Service. To accept these undertakings meant that I was a frequent traveller on the 7 a.m. plane to London and the six day working week became a seven day working week to meet these new commitments.

THE CENTRAL HEALTH SERVICES COUNCIL

The Central Health Services Council was set up by the Minister of

State/Health to advise the Government on all aspects of health care. This council was well constituted and had members associated with the government, the medical and related professions, and the civil service. It had advisory committees and in particular a standing medical advisory committee under the chairmanship of Sir Ronald Gibson.* The council was therefore competent and well informed to help to guide the National Health Service.

Five years' service on this committee gave me a broader and more national outlook on the Health Service and its problems and personalities. There were occasions however when I felt the council bowed in deference to the permanent civil service and was reminiscent of the T.V. series *Yes Prime Minister*. For some time I had been anxious about the increase in the number of administrators in the hospital service and the consequent bureaucracy that had been set up. I raised this in the council at a time when Barbara Castle was Secretary of State for Social Services and Dr David Owen (now Lord Owen) was Under Secretary at the Department of Health and Social Security.

All members listened very carefully to all that I had to say and the only comment was that of Dr Owen who said that there could not be yet another re-organization of the National Health Service. No one else said a single word and not even one of my well-known medical colleagues spoke.

I was to learn from this experience that an idea or suggestion can be stopped, not by open opposition, but by being absorbed in silence. This is a process which I have since observed in many other fields.

CENTRAL COUNCIL FOR POSTGRADUATE MEDICAL EDUCATION

The rapid advances in all branches of medicine means that qualification is only the first stage in what must be a continuing educational process. This has been fully realized by the medical profession and it is a measure of the importance of this to the patient, that many doctors were included as members of this council. The idea of a central council was to act as a focus and initiator of general Postgraduate Medical Education, which

---

* Sir Ronald Gibson, General Practitioner, Winchester, Past President of B.M.A.

would be regionalized at the provincial universities where Postgraduate Committees were to be set up. This central body was to diminish in activity as the regional centres began to develop. It is a great satisfaction to see Postgraduate Medical Education flourish now in each of the fourteen regions.

THE ROYAL COLLEGE OF SURGEONS

True to its long traditions the Royal College of Surgeons not only makes a major contribution to the encouragement of academic surgery but also is very concerned to maintain the standards of practical surgery. The colleges have for very many years approved certain hospital posts as part of the requirements for obtaining the F.R.C.S. qualification.

In post-war years a major extension of this principal has been instituted for candidates who are proceeding for further training to attain consultant posts. Specialist Advisory Committees have been set up, in various surgical specialities, to review more senior hospital training posts which are those normally held by a senior registrar. This means that specialist training can be supervised until the candidate attains recognition as a specialist.

I had the good fortune to be elected to the Specialist Advisory Committee in General Surgery. The duties of this post were to visit certain selected hospitals, to consider the clinical workload, the facilities in staffing, and to interview the senior registrars who were in advanced training. Interviews were also held with the consultant staff who were responsible for the training of their junior colleagues. To do this a panel of three surgeons visited various regions to carry out this very important review and to make recommendations regarding the training programmes.

I was involved in two areas, that involving the London Teaching Hospitals north of the Thames, and also the East Anglian Region surrounding Cambridge. The visits to these hospitals was a most fascinating experience, for it provided a very close contact with the surgeons to observe their merit and to see the work they were doing. In addition individual interviews were held with the senior registrars and it is interesting to note that many of these now have become distinguished consultant surgeons in this and in other countries. It was impressive to see the work being done at the London Teaching Schools, many of which are much

of these distinguished hospitals, while providing some very specialized training, however did not have sufficient clinical material to provide a broad basis for general surgical training.

This shortage of general surgical patients has been due to the development of the District General Hospitals which now do the major part of the surgical work in Britain. It was also noted that in central London there was a shortage of experience in emergency surgery, since the city does not have a high night population. It seemed necessary therefore that certain Teaching Hospitals should combine with others to produce an adequate surgical programme and this was emphasized in my reports to the Royal Colleges.

This feature has again been highlighted two decades later by the publication of the Tomlinson Report now under discussion. Our own reports to the College were constructive and took into consideration many features and suggestions made during our visits by the consultant staff and their senior registrars.

In one case only was a completely adverse report submitted regarding the training in a famous hospital in the East Anglian Region. This caused consternation to some of the consultants, but on review of this training programme a year later it still failed to gain our approval. This decision which was fully justified by a subsequent personal tragic surgical experience which occurred in this very hospital.

It is perhaps important to emphasize in the public interest the intense care and planning that the Royal Colleges of Surgeons have given to surgical training. It requires a programme of specialist training for a minimum of four years after a similar period in general surgical training. A specialist therefore requires a minimum of ten years postgraduate training before a candidate can be considered for a surgical appointment. Today there is much talk of reducing the hours of work and the period of training on the grounds that better planning of training will compensate for these changes. It is my belief that a shorter period of training and shorter hours will reduce the standard of surgical expertise, and that such changes are not likely to produce the master surgeons of former years. It is to be hoped that Common Market regulations will not lower the standard that we have set in Britain and the training period be reduced. The position today in our profession is very different from that in former years, the years of Cronin's *The Citadel*.

THE BRITISH MEDICAL ASSOCIATION

The British Medical Association, much criticized by the politicians as the doctors' Trade Union, is in fact a very much more sophisticated body. Many facets of its work are for the protection of the public as well as the protection of the profession and for this it has set up many committees.

Perhaps one of the most interesting of these is the Board of Science and Education. I had the privilege of serving on this committee under the chairmanships of Sir John Peel, Sir John Stallworthy and Sir Douglas Black. The committee dealt with scientific advances in medicines and their relationship not only to research, but also to the day to day management of the ordinary patient.

It was indeed a great pleasure to serve in this committee under, in the first instance, the chairmanship of Sir John Peel. This took my mind back many years to the time that I first met him when I was a surgeon in the Emergency Medical Service at King's College Hospital where he was the Consultant Gynaecologist. Those were the days of the bombing of London and were grim indeed. But in spite of all the hardship there were some light-hearted moments. During this period of the war John had just seen my wife and confirmed that she was expecting a baby.

As was the custom at the time all the staff had meals together at the hospital. In the course of light-hearted lunchtime conversation Dr Sidney Thompson, the Consultant Dermatologist said he would give £5 to the next member of staff who had a child. John Peel, who had just examined Joan and confirmed that she was pregnant, looked up at me with smiling eyes and we both laughed in our minds but our faces remained unchanged as we alone shared this secret. Sidney Thompson was soon to lose £10, on the arrival of twin boys.

Almost thirty years later it was interesting to sit on the Board of Science in the peace and safety of the British Medical Association Headquarters in Tavistock House and to reflect on those dark days.

But new clouds were appearing on the horizon. Russia and the West had embarked on a policy of nuclear re-armament and the B.M.A. had commissioned the Board of Science to provide an objective and scientific account of the medical consequences which could follow the explosion of nuclear weapons.

A small working party was set up* to receive written and oral evidence from experts in many fields. This committee sat for a period of two years before producing its report on the medical effects of Nuclear War.[29]

The historical reports of the destruction of Nagasaki on 9 August 1945 and that of Hiroshima were beyond belief. In Hiroshima out of a population of 350,000 people, 130,000 were killed or died soon after the single attack. In Nagasaki, a city of 270,000, sixty to seventy thousand were dead at the end of 1945. What was even more disturbing was the fact that the bombs used in these attacks were very small compared with those available today.

The immediate effect of the nuclear explosions in blast, heat, hurricane winds, and irradiation were fully discussed, but what was more disturbing still was the long-term effects on the atmosphere. As the result of nuclear bombing, quantities of sunlight-absorbing particles would enter the atmosphere (troposphere) and would restrict the heat of the sun and the planet would cool and produce a second Ice Age.

On the other hand destruction of the ozone layer would subsequently cause overheating. It is interesting to note that a decade after the B.M.A. report and in another context, attention is now being drawn to the effects of destruction of the ozone layer and of global warming.

The general impression gained by this two year study was that nuclear war would not only destroy countries and continents, but would destroy the planet. It is perhaps true to say that the idea of nuclear war is unthinkable and retaining nuclear weapons as a deterrent is solely in the hope of preserving peace, and to prevent the possibility of nuclear blackmail by some petty dictator. Should the West be so foolish as to follow the policy advocated by C.N.D. and give up nuclear weapons then they could be subject to blackmail and would have to submit to whatever demands were made upon it.

In most recent times, perhaps due to a realization of the global consequences of the use of nuclear weapons, Russia and the United States have embarked on a programme of reducing the stock pile of weapons of mass destruction. Perhaps in this respect the Board of Science of the B.M.A. has made a major contribution to the peace process.

---

* Sir John Stallworthy; Dr Stuart J. Horner; Mr Kenneth McKeown, C.B.E.; Professor Peter Quilliam, O.B.E.; Dr John Dawson

22

The Carlton Club

THE primary purpose of the hospital service is in the diagnosis and treatment of serious disease and injury. Social and domestic factors are more in the province of the general practitioner. At the same time the hospital consultant cannot be unaware that political factors do intrude on their work, and they inevitably take some interest in political and organizational matters.

In the midst of the many visits to London there was one visit that was quite unique in that it was a solitary visit and that it was at the invitation of a politician. Sir Timothy Kitson the Member of Parliament for Richmond (Yorks) had a very great interest in hospitals and in the Health Service. We had many discussions and it was the hope of many here that he would become the Minister of Health. He asked me if I would come with him to the Carlton Club and give some of his colleagues my views on the hospital service.

It was my first and only visit to the club and took place on the 28 April 1969. At the club I was to meet Maurice MacMillan. Paul Dean, Lord Balneil and other members of parliament who were specially interested in the National Health Service.

It was at a time when the Socialist party were very much against private practice in the hospital service and had done everything possible to limit or remove private beds in the National Health Service Hospitals. It was their intention to introduce a full time salaried medical service.

At this time many consultants were employed in what was called Maximum Part-time Contracts in which they did nine-elevenths of their time in the National Health Service allowing two-elevenths of their time for private practice. In actual fact most surgeons did night and week-end emergency sessions for which they did not seek or indeed receive any payment whatever.

The part-time consultants did virtually full time work in the National Health Service and did their private work in any spare time that was available. The government got a real bargain from the services of part-time consultants.

The major issue at this time seemed to be private practice and even some Tory politicians were not very favourably disposed to private practice within the National Health Service. My own views evolved after over twenty years in consultant practice were simple and straight forward and involved three features.

The first was that private practice should be preserved inside the National Health Service. This would encourage money to stay within the service to meet the demands presented by medical advances and the expenses induced by more sophisticated medical treatment. As a protection for the general population using the N.H.S. the number of private beds should be controllable and limited to say ten per cent, which would be politically acceptable.

Maurice MacMillan asked me a question that was tinged with the doubt lingering in the minds of some Tory politicians. He asked, "How can you justify private practice within the N.H.S.?" I simply replied by stating that the better care I gave to my N.H.S. patients the larger my private practice would become.

I assured him that over ninety per cent of my time was spent in the N.H.S. work and that less than ten per cent was spent on private patients. Yet it should be noted that the income from private patients who absorbed so little time, was greater than that received from the much greater time spent on the National Health Service.

My second suggestion was that the income recovered from the private beds should be retained as "free monies" by the Management Committees. This would mean that funds would be available for local improvements in the service as would seem to be expedient. It would also mean that money could be held over from one year to another so that even major capital schemes, such as building a new wing at the hospital, could be carried out without trying to get capital allocations from the Regional Hospital Board.

It was my experience on the Management Committee that at the end of the financial year, in order not to lose funds, money would be spent on non-essential fields, as money could not be retained for the following year. There was a further advantage in this suggestion in that those Management Committees who, for political or other reasons, were adverse to private practice did not have to be involved in the scheme. The loss of finance however might well induce them to change their minds when they realized that private practice, far from restricting the National Health Service, was helping it financially and diminishing the pressure on N.H.S. beds which then became more available as some patients opted to be private patients.

The third suggestion was made in order to harness private insurance schemes and to utilise their advantages so far as possible within the National Health Service. This suggestion was a corollary of the other two suggestions. A patient insured with a provident insurance scheme (such as BUPA, PPP and WPA) is still, as a taxpayer, fully entitled to a hospital bed within the National Health Service. If he is willing to forego this right and accept private treatment he will release a much needed bed for an N.H.S. patient. In addition, should he be admitted to one of the limited number of private beds, then the income derived from this bed would go into the pool of free monies.

To encourage this scheme it was argued that sickness insurance premiums should be a tax allowable expense. This seemed to be entirely fair and benefited the patient, the hospital and the consultant. At the end of our discussions at the Carlton Club I wrote a summary of the meeting and quite recently came across this letter. On reading it, it is indeed most relevant to the problems that the National Health Service is encountering today.

The essential concept was to encourage private practice, but to allow it to develop within the N.H.S. and not as an independent and separate development. It would therefore keep money within the Health Service and not let it filter away to private sources. Clinical advances which have constantly been taking place have increased the possibilities of new treatments and the expectations of the patients, but unfortunately Health Service policies have done nothing to provide the money to finance such treatments. Further medical advance will produce further financial problems.

If only these three simple concepts had been put into practice as I suggested at the Carlton Club twenty years ago what a great advance would have been attained. To meet the increasing success of medicine, governments of all political shades have instituted one re-organization after another, with an ever increasing bureaucracy and little if any success.

The present state of unhappy turmoil, with morale at rock bottom could have been avoided by the institution of these simple concepts which would have gone a long way to meet the financial consequences of medical advances and success. Unfortunately, simple concepts are so difficult to understand.

23

The Local Medical Scene

IN the time of Cronin's *The Citadel* medical excellence was concentrated in the great centres of knowledge and of skill. Edinburgh with its elegance, its university, and its Royal College was the Scottish centre. London with its many medical schools, its teaching hospitals and its metropolitan atmosphere was a medical mecca. But times have changed and in the past half century excellence has become multi-centric. No longer have the great centres a monopoly of skills, because the provincial medical schools and the district general hospitals can match or even surpass these former centres of excellence.

A close association with London and Edinburgh enabled me to have not only a peripheral but also a central view of surgical practice. In these circumstances it is possible to identify the essence of clinical excellence, and to relegate ancillary influences to their proper position. The standard of medical practice is determined largely by what goes on between the patient and the clinician.

In surgery it is the knowledge, judgement and operative skill of the surgeon that determines the future of the patient. The operative risk (mortality) is related largely to technical excellence. In cancer surgery it is now becoming realized that not only immediate operative mortality rate but even long-term survival can depend on the operative skills of atraumatic surgery. It must be realized that the key feature of medicine is not in its administration or management but in the professional skill which is the paramount feature.

In the last half century while the clinicians have been struggling for clinical excellence, administration has proliferated enormously and the titles of the administrators have become more impressive and in some cases bizarre. Administrative value, however, must be assessed by the way in which it facilitates the work of the doctor.

In hospital practice, nursing and secretarial assistance are of greater value than the administrative structure however ingenious. It should always be remembered that if all the administrators were suddenly to diminish or even disappear, as happened in medicine during the last war, the healing of the sick would continue much the same.

The importance of the administrator is in acting as a catalyst and this is a concept that has to be emphasized. Administrators should be like the spokes of a wheel but at the centre is the clinician and his patient which is the hub of medical practice. Administration or management is a means to an end and not an end in itself.

Management must be judged in how it helps clinical practice. Control or dictatorship is not one of its functions in the National Health Service.

While convalescing at Lyme Regis after an operation in 1958 I was walking near a little stream in very, very cold weather. In a pool there was a mini-iceberg which was floating in the stream. It struck me at the time that there was a remarkable analogy between an iceberg and an administrator. An iceberg remains cold and is largely submerged, but it moves with the stream, is affected by undercurrents but melts when it gets into hot water.

In one of my own hospitals the administrator remained unseen and spent much time in trying to interpret the trends and undercurrents of thought which might be to his advantage. When things got really tough and hot he vanished and left no trace.

I saw the future of medicine in the attainment of knowledge and of skills and one hopes that in future administration will see its proper role as an ancillary and complementary one. It should not be a controlling factor because medical care is on a different plane and can not be attained without doctors and nurses.

Most of the observations of development outlined here are perhaps more hospital orientated rather than approached from the point of view of the general practitioner. But general practice, too, has changed and is still changing. When I started consultant practice in the North East it was noticeable the very close relationship the doctor had with his patient. This was much more close than I had experienced while practising in London. In the Yorkshire Dales and in the small towns of the North

Riding of Yorkshire, the standard of practice was high indeed and the continuity of medical supervision first class. Each doctor knew each of his patients and from past knowledge was able to discern the first signs of failure of health and the development of serious disease.

Practices were small and often there were only two doctors, the practitioner and his assistant or junior partner. This system seemed to work well but has been slowly eroded over the years. Practices have become amalgamated and the numbers of doctors in any one practice increased so that the patients relationship with the doctor has become less individual and not so close. The present trend is to have large practices and large lists of patients.

As a hospital consultant one's role is to help and assist the general practitioner and to serve his patients. The general practitioner's function is health promotion but also to identify early symptoms of serious disease and to refer such cases to hospital for treatment. In the Darlington and Northallerton areas the two aspects of medical practice worked in close accord and harmony. In very recent years the latest trends in the National Health Service threaten to break down an accord and the team-work which has so successfully been built up in the past decades.

In attempting to attain the highest standards of surgical practice, techniques and procedures were given constant thought and evolutionary changes took place. In this atmosphere the so called "surgical audit" seems rather strangely irrelevant and artificial. It is true to say that in former years the patients tended to stay in hospital over long, but this was due to caution and to the fact that domiciliary back up was not so good as it is today. It now seems that the pendulum has swung too much in the opposite direction and that patients are now kept in hospital for too short a time and the major pressure is to get them home and to close wards.

There is, for example, a tendency almost amounting to a craze for day surgery and even expensive new hospital wings are constructed for this purpose. While it is agreed that much minor surgery can be done on an out-patient basis certain procedures, for example, rupture operations (hernias) are being done as day cases. As a patient who recently had an operation of this type I must confess that I would not like to have gone home the day of operation and to have spent the first night accompanied by an anxious wife and a painful scar. This is an example of political and financial considerations taking precedence over clinical need.

Years of consultant experience have shown that all clinical needs cannot instantly be met and that some selective process must be used in hospital admissions. Throughout these years patients were admitted on grounds of clinical priority. Budgetary and financial considerations and the attainment of irrelevant and artificial targets fortunately at this time did not intrude in hospital work. Selection of cases for admission was left in the competent hands of the professionals without lay interference.

The surgical work was hard and long but rewarding. There was a team work between doctors and nurses which was commendable, and no members of staff ever questioned working for longer hours as there was such job satisfaction.

There was, of course, a changing pattern of work and as one problem appeared to be solved other problems presented fresh challenges. Fortunately at this time statistics (that other form of lies) had not been elevated to the point where they could dictate policy and treatment, as appears to be the case in the hospital of today. Most truth is realized in retrospect and in looking back over the years 1950–1977 these were indeed the halcyon days.

24

Retirement

MANY people look forward so much to retirement that they lose sight of the present and waste part of their lifetime in expectation. I had never looked forward to retirement nor had I made any special plans as to what I would do when I stopped my work as a surgeon. The few years coming up to retirement passed with unbelievable speed and I came to realize that with advancing age time seems to accelerate. When one was young the long summer holidays of school days stretched out for an eternity but in later life a summer soon passes. And so it was that the date of retirement came with great speed and it was necessary to take stock for the future.

In biology the most important event is the passing on of genes, and in life itself the most important function is to pass on knowledge and experience. In human behaviour little is learned from one generation to the next and everyone begins life from the same base line of lack of experience.

In science it is entirely different and the work of yesterday forms the basis of the work of today, while today's work forms the basis of the work of tomorrow. Real progress is made by building on previous experience.

As my retirement approached I realized that I would like to pass on to my successors the experience that I had gained over the years particularly in the surgery of peptic ulcer and that of cancer of the oesophagus. Though many surgical societies and almost 300 individual surgeons had visited my unit in Darlington I still had many enquiries and a waiting list of surgical guests. I was anxious not to disappoint my colleagues from all over the world and was anxious to make an arrangement that would allow me to continue to demonstrate these techniques.

I suggested to my surgical colleagues that I would like to continue, in an entirely voluntary and unpaid capacity, to do some oesophageal surgery so that more surgeons would have the opportunity of learning these new techniques.

As the new hospital building programme at Darlington had, for various reasons, resulted in an over production of hospital beds, bed space would therefore be no problem. In fact the new orthopaedic wing was at this time about to become disused, and I felt that this accommodation would provide the facility for the development of a special oesophageal unit which could accommodate all cases of cancer of the oesophagus from the Northern region. The opportunity seemed too good to miss and if grasped would establish Darlington as a leading centre in oesophageal surgery far into the future.

I put the case to my colleagues in Darlington and the matter was discussed at the Medical Advisory Committee that was held in January 1977. To my very great regret my two surgical colleagues absolutely refused to support the suggestion and insisted that I should stop all work in Darlington Memorial Hospital. And so it was that the most wonderful opportunity for Darlington Memorial Hospital to become a centre of excellence in this field was lost forever.

It is interesting but sad to note that, as already mentioned, at the very time I had the honour to be speaking at the Civic Reception for oesophageal surgeons in Cape Town, my surgical colleagues in Darlington were discarding an opportunity that came only once in a lifetime.

As the years pass by the short-sightedness of this dreadful decision has become painfully apparent, and the failure to grasp this opportunity even more tragic. As I had anticipated the international reputation in oesophageal surgery gained in Darlington melted away in a sudden thaw, and left a clinical scene of only a few patients with oesophageal cancer. The long stream of visiting surgeons stopped, and the gap was never filled. Strangely enough no outstanding centre for oesophageal cancer has been established in the North, and the role that Darlington could have played in this field was destroyed by the decision of the Medical Advisory Committee in 1977.

But errors and mistakes have a knock on effect. One of my anaesthe-

FIGURE 30. *Speakers at Valedictory Seminar.*
(Left to right): Professor Reginald Hall, Professor of Medicine, University of Newcastle-upon-Tyne; Sir Rodney (now Lord) Smith, then President of the Royal College of Surgeons of England; author; Mr William Michie, M.B.E., Senior Surgeon, Aberdeen Royal Infirmary; Mr James Ross, M.B.E., President of the Royal College of Surgeons of Edinburgh.

tists, Dr David Bishop, showed a special interest in the anaesthetic problems associated with operations for cancer of the oesophagus. In these operations the chest is opened, and the function of the lungs modified. Dr Bishop, with commendable enthusiasm and interest, carried out some research in this field and published a paper on this subject which was one of great merit and interest.[30]

This research was the beginning of what could have been an on-going study, but sadly with the disappearance of Darlington as a leading oesophageal centre, these research studies have had to be abandoned, and the loss is great.

October is the month of my birth and Halloween the day, so that the 31 October has always been a time of interest and in this respect the year 1977 was no exception. My farewell to Darlington took the form of a

Valedictory Seminar. In arranging this special seminar I am most grateful to one of my colleagues, Dr Ian Martin, the Consultant Psychiatrist and to my secretary Eileen Raine. The programme was drawn up with the artistry and elegance that only Ian Martin could produce and the efficiency that Eileen always employed. The speakers were chosen with very great care and with much thought and appropriate consideration. It was felt most important that they be chosen not only as being representative of British surgery but also because of their individual distinction. The speakers were Sir Rodney Smith (now Lord Smith), James Ross, William Michie and Professor Reginald Hall, C.B.E. (Fig. 30).

Sir Rodney was President of the Royal College of Surgeons of England and I had met him many years previously when I first watched him operate at St. George's Hospital in London. On this occasion he was removing the pancreas for a malignant tumour and I was most impressed with his courage in tackling this type of extremely difficult major surgery of which he was to become a pioneer. In subsequent years we met at various Royal College Committees and functions and I was honoured that he accepted the invitation to speak.

James Ross, M.B.E. was President of the Royal College of Surgeons of Edinburgh, a college to which he contributed great distinction. He was an authority on certain special aspects of urology (urinary disease) and it was on the surgical aspects of disease of the ureter that he gave his address. It was he who enthusiastically accepted the donation of the McKeown Medal to be awarded each year to the Edinburgh College Lecturer.

William Michie, M.B.E., was the senior surgeon at the Royal Infirmary in Aberdeen and a past President of the Association of Surgeons of Great Britain. He was an authority on thyroid and parathyroid surgery. We had spent many hours together on the surgical panels that reviewed training programmes for the Specialist Advisory Committee of the Royal Colleges. I particularly appreciated his acceptance of this invitation as he knew at this very time that he was terminally ill. His address was excellent and was delivered with fortitude and great courage. It was with great sadness to all of us in British surgery that we heard of his death so shortly after this seminar.

The choice of Professor Reginald Hall was very special in that he was from the University of Newcastle-upon-Tyne and was the only physician to be asked to speak. His concepts of thyroid disease (goitre of various types) were years ahead of his time and his contribution was outstanding and complemented that of William Michie.

It was my hope that we could invite Professor R. B. Welbourn from Hammersmith Hospital whose work on endocrine surgery, (the surgery of the glands that control the function of the body) was so outstanding but it was felt that a fifth guest speaker would be difficult to fit in without encroachment on the other speakers. It was with very great regret that he could not be included in the speakers.

My own valedictory address was a distillate of the work developed and done in the Memorial Hospital in Darlington and in the Friarage and Rutson Hospitals in Northallerton. It was concerned mainly with the surgical treatment of duodenal and gastric ulcer, of the new operations for cancer of the gullet, and with some clinical and experimental work on various problems related to general surgery including ileo-rectal anastomosis in ulcerative colitis.

FIGURE 31. *Guests at Farewell Dinner.*
(Right to left): Sir John Peel, K.C.V.O, Gynaecologist to H. M. The Queen; Joan McKeown; Lord Smith, Past President of the Royal College of Surgeons of England; Lady Tranmire; the author.

236

It is always a pleasure to listen to a master surgeon give an address on any subject, but to hear such a surgeon talking on his favourite subject is indeed a double pleasure. There was a theme of excellence and interest from each guest speaker which was captured by David Baxter of the pharmaceutical company of Geistlich in an excellent book recording the proceedings of the Valedictory Seminar. So well did he do his task of editor that the book soon ran out of print and a new edition is urgently needed.

During the height of activity of a surgeon's life there is limited time and opportunity to entertain colleagues and to make deep friendships. Realizing that many of our friends and colleagues had been somewhat neglected I decided to have a special Valedictory Dinner and to invite just under 100 special guests. The dinner was held in the Europa Hotel, a very pleasant hotel in Darlington surrounded by extensive well-kept gardens and a golf course. The hotel had gained some notoriety by the fact that talks were held there by Lord Whitelaw and the Ulster politicians in an attempt to solve a problem that started at the time of my childhood and which today still remains unsolved.

The private dining room was galleried and decorated by heraldic symbols which seemed so appropriate to the occasion. The guests were from my native Ulster, from London where I had trained for fifteen years, and from the North East where I settled with such pleasure and with no regrets. It was a wonderful experience to be able to entertain my colleagues, my friends and selected members of the hospital staff who had worked so hard and so loyally for up to twenty-seven years. It gave me the opportunity to acknowledge in public how much I appreciated their help over many difficult years. (Fig. 31)

25

After Retirement

NOVEMBER is the herald of the season of mists and a reminder that the year is drawing to its close. But it was for me, in 1977, also the season of mellow fruitfulness, where the work of an entire career could be reviewed and contemplated. It presented the opportunity for completing some projects which, because of the shortage of time, had never been brought to fruition.

In retirement from a very busy and demanding surgical practice the feeling of not having to get up early to tackle a full day of surgical work is strange indeed. For me it produced an odd feeling of emptiness when the hectic life in the National Health Service stopped on Halloween, 1977. In the strange days of this particular autumn the realization that retirement is the beginning of a new opportunity slowly dawned.

Retirement provided the opportunity to do things that I had wanted to do for so long and it seemed important that this opportunity should not be missed. It seemed that active surgical practice would cease and that I would never operate again but would divert my attention to other activities and to my other interests. But this was not to be the case. Involvement in new hospital developments, surgical writing, demonstrating operative techniques and lecturing were to make retirement fruitful and rewarding.

SCORTON HOSPITAL

As so often happens in life the unexpected event suddenly occurs and the future is changed. This is indeed what happened. Quite unexpectedly

I was approached by the Provincial of the Order of St. John of God and by Sir Timothy Kitson, M.P.* to ask me if I would join the Trustees of the Hospital at Scorton. I was very surprised that an Ulster Protestant should be asked to join a Catholic Order and I found the idea quite novel and exciting. I said "yes" quite gladly and was delighted to accept this invitation and indeed have served as a Trustee from that time just until the present day.

In former years Scorton Hospital had been largely financed by grants from the Northallerton Health Authority, and this combined with private donations had enabled the hospital to provide complementary and supplementary medical services alongside those provided by the National Health Service. With the development of a large new District General Hospital in Darlington and further development of the Friarage Hospital in Northallerton the need for the services of Scorton began to diminish, and the Health Authority at Northallerton began to phase out their financial support.

Scorton Hospital, therefore, became threatened with closure as an acute hospital which would have meant that it would revert to its former function which was largely to do with the care of the chronic sick. The Order of St. John of God were anxious that the hospital should survive and develop as an acute hospital and it was for this reason that I was asked to become a Trustee. The hospital was certainly in a situation of crisis both from the professional and from the financial points of view.

To meet this situation the Order had planned to set up a rehabilitation unit with particular reference to industrial injuries. It had been hoped that workmen injured in the industrial heartland of Teesside could come to Scorton for specialist treatment to enable them to return to their normal work.

A unit was designed on most modern lines and was lavish in its provision of equipment and facilities. In due course this centre was opened by Her Majesty the Queen Mother in 1977. Unfortunately this scheme, though ambitious in concept was not successful for a variety of reasons. It was therefore necessary that, for the continuation of Scorton Hospital as an acute hospital, it had to provide other services.

---

* Sir Timothy Kitson. Formerly Member of Parliament for Richmond (North Yorkshire) and Private Parliamentary Secretary to Prime Minister Edward Heath.

At this particular time of crisis, private practice in medicine was opposed by the socialist politicians, and even some of the conservatives were reluctant to approve of private practice. They were slow to appreciate the importance of realizing that a private sector could contribute greatly to the welfare of the Health Service. I felt, however, that the only source of income that would ensure the continuation of Scorton Hospital was from private practice and that the most effective contribution I could make to Scorton was to continue in private practice and to use Scorton as a private hospital.

It was, however, necessary to develop private beds in the hospital and this was the task to which Sir Timothy Kitson and the Trustees set to work. Due largely to Sir Timothy's influence and hard work the private wing known as "the middle floor" was soon in operation and a new phase and philosophy was to develop in Scorton. Though it was not thought of and could not have been anticipated at this time, the subsequent development of the philosophy of Mrs. Thatcher was to work greatly to the advantage of the hospital.

This new and completely unexpected development came just at the very time when I had experienced the greatest disappointment of my entire professional life.

As already mentioned the idea of the development of an oesophageal unit in Darlington Memorial Hospital was uppermost in my mind. I felt that the establishment of such a unit of excellence would have been wonderful for Darlington and for Britain. To have such an idea and concept turned down by some of my surgical colleagues was indeed a devastating experience. The skills of the operating theatre teams and of the ward staff were of the highest order and a whole newly built hospital wing at Darlington Memorial Hospital had been vacated so that everything was perfect for this exciting venture in oesophageal surgery.

But this, the darkest cloud of my surgical career had a silver lining, because I realized that by working at Scorton in private practice I could now have the financial resources to accept invitations from abroad to speak on the developments of oesophageal surgery that had taken place in Darlington over the previous twenty-seven years. Instead of the surgeons coming to Darlington, which would have been ideal for Britain, I could now go abroad and travel the entire world to talk on these new developments.

When I was no longer allowed to operate in Darlington Memorial Hospital, the key staff of the operating theatre without even being asked decided to come to Scorton and to develop the theatre work there to the supreme standard which they had already attained in Darlington and indeed in Northallerton. I am most grateful to Sister Hilary Atkinson and to Nurse Graham, and later to Sister Potts for their loyalty and their support. Joined by Alex Takacs the technician they formed a great team.

The surgical work in Scorton developed and flourished and the income to the Order solved their financial problems. As time went on and as the result of Thatcherism, private practice was to develop even more, with this and with the advent of a wider field in surgery, the future of Scorton Hospital was secure.

Though much work in Scorton was routine there were occasions when patients from foreign countries added an unusual spice to life. An Arab from Saudi Arabia came to have a cancer of his gullet removed. He and his retinue arrived with turbans in gay colours and flowing galabeas which indeed provided a most colourful sight. I had been used, while on service in the Middle East, to deal with Arab patients in the grey, sandy background of the North African desert or in the sands of Egypt.

To see this great splash of colour on the green agricultural background of the North Riding of Yorkshire was indeed quite startling. Arab culture has changed little in the past 2,000 years, and just as the three wise men were bringing gifts of gold, frankincense and myrrh to greet the arrival of the Messiah, so this patient's relatives, armed with various eastern gifts, came to meet me and to introduce the patient. I felt convinced that this galaxy of gifts was to ensure that the patient had the very best treatment.

The patient himself could not speak a word of English, but it was remarkable how well the nurses handled this situation. Even the deep segregation of the sexes in Arab custom seemed to be overcome by the staff and his post-operative management was smooth and successful.

His relatives were accommodated in the top floor of the hospital which was part of the quarters allocated to the Brothers of St. John. The quarters were furnished elegantly in western style but the comfortable chairs and settees were discarded by the Arabs and the entire retinue sat on the floor in the usual cross-legged Arab position which I had seen so many years before. With the discharge of the patient and his retinue we all felt a certain loss at the departure of these colourful characters.

It was for me a great pleasure to be able to continue my operative work at Scorton Hospital. It had always been my ambition to attain perfection in operative technique, and in the hands of really great surgeons any operation appears simple. It was apparent too that operative mortality was inversely proportional to the excellence of the operative technique and most post-operative deaths were due to errors of technique.

In recent years the possibility that long-term survival in cancer surgery may also be related to operative excellence has at long last become realized. In the gentler atmosphere of retirement there was more time to contemplate the importance of operative technique, and to oppose and negate the idea that had arisen in certain areas of academic surgery, that operative surgery was of subsidiary importance.

TEXTBOOKS IN SURGERY

With the establishment of District General Hospitals the whole emphasis of the surgical work-load in Great Britain underwent a complete change. In former years the London and the Provincial Teaching Hospitals did most of the major surgery throughout Britain.

As surgical and medical talents became dispersed from the Teaching Schools to the District General Hospitals, the patients were happy to accept a local consultant service which was equal to, or in some centres, better than that obtained from the more major centres. The establishment of a hip replacement centre by Sir John Charmley in Wigan was an example of surgical excellence in the District General Hospital. A further example is the work of Sir Magdi Yacoub, the cardiac surgeon at Harefield Hospital.

The volume and variety of work in the District General Hospital has become so great that time for discussion and for the writing up of results has been very limited. The District General Hospital has also in the past lacked the supporting structure that made publication much more easy in the Teaching Hospitals. Much to my regret pressure of work in the past had limited my own publications to a bare minimum, but retirement offered the opportunity to publish results and to contribute sections to textbooks of surgery on subjects which had become a life long study.

At the invitation of Selwyn Taylor,* an old friend of mine from my London days, I was happy to contribute a chapter on "Diseases of the Oesophagus" in his most recent textbook *Surgical Management*.[31] This chapter dealt with all aspects of surgical disease of the oesophagus and was a sequel to a chapter on "Carcinoma of the Oesophagus" in *Recent Advances in Surgery*[32] which had been edited by Selwyn Taylor with equal distinction ten years previously. British surgery owes a great deal to Selwyn Taylor for the excellence of all the surgical publications with which he has been involved.

During a visit to Chicago to give a lecture and to show a film on cancer of the oesophagus, I had the great pleasure of meeting a very distinguished American Surgeon called Lloyd Nyhus. He was the Warren H. Cole Professor of Surgery in the University of Illinois at Chicago and stood head and shoulders above his other colleagues.

We talked quite a lot together and had a strong common interest in the surgical treatment of duodenal and gastric ulcer, a subject on which he is a world authority. Having seen my film of the special three-phase operation for cancer of the gullet which had first been done and developed in Northallerton and Darlington, he asked me to write a chapter in his book, *Mastery of Surgery* and to describe my operation.[33] This is a very special and unusual textbook where world authorities write a chapter on a subject of their special interest and it gave me great pleasure to make a contribution.[33]

Some twenty years ago, a very famous British surgeon called Ronald Raven,† formed a new society of surgeons who had a special interest in the treatment of cancer. The society was called the British Association of Surgical Oncology and I was delighted to be invited to be one of its founder members. The society has thrived and has now expanded its interests in Europe and there has now been formed a European Society

---

* Selwyn Taylor. Consultant Surgeon. King's College Hospital. Dean Ereitus and Fellow of Royal Postgraduate Medical School, Hammersmith Hospital, London.
† Ronald Raven, O.B.E., T.D., O.St.K., F.R.C.S., Hon. Consultant Surgeon Royal Marsden Hospital and Institute of Cancer Research, London

of Surgical Oncology. With the development of surgical oncology, Ian Burn[*] has been a major influence.

Ronald Raven was most anxious to publish a textbook concerned especially with the techniques for cancer operations. After much delay this book has now been completed under the editorship of Ian Burn and J. McK Wellwood[34] and the first volume has just been published. It has been a great pleasure to contribute the first chapter of Volume 1 and to be able to describe in detail the operations for cancer of the gullet devised and developed at the Friarage Hospital in Northallerton and in the Memorial Hospital in Darlington.

CONTEMPLATION AND REFLECTION

The pressures of day to day work greatly restrict the opportunities for contemplation and reflection. Retirement, however, provides an opportunity for thought and even for philosophy.

In dealing with cancer patients, surgeons take great care to examine the growth, to have microscopic sections taken to determine its structure and to assess its extent. The process is referred to as "grading and staging" and is used as a measure to assess the outlook in the individual case and the prospects of success with treatment. It is true to say that in cases in which the grading and staging is unfavourable the outlook is usually gloomy.

There is, however, one feature that struck me over the many years that I looked after cancer patients and that is, that all cases in unfavourable grades and stages do not always do badly while those in good grades do not always do well.

I remember one patient in particular who had a cancer of the stomach discovered accidentally when having an operation for gall stones. This cancer was perhaps the earliest that I have ever seen, and she did have a most effective operation for its removal. In spite of what appeared to be a most favourable circumstance this case did extremely badly.

I felt that the explanation of these features was concerned with the

---

[*] Ian Burn F.R.C.S., Consultant Surgeon, Charing Cross Hospital, and Director of Surgical Studies, Hammersmith Hospital, London.

FIGURE 32. *The Ivor Lewis Memorial Lecture.*
(Left to right): Sir Geoffrey Slaney, President of the Royal College of Surgeons of England; Dr Buddug Owen, Consultant Anaesthetist; the author; Mr Christopher Davies, Consultant Surgeon, North Wales.

patient's own resistance against the malignant process. In this respect the patient's own defence and resistance against the growth seems to be important and this concept has now entered the popular press in describing various celebrities in their "fight" against cancer. This feature of the patient's own resistance to growths is highlighted in the recent contribution to the surgical literature.[25]

EPONYMOUS LECTURES

Various famous surgeons have had their work recognized by the establishment of a lecture to a learned society which bears their name. To be invited to give such a lecture is of special interest in that it involves research into the life and work of the named person and it also enables the lecturer to choose a subject of his own special interest. It has been

245

my privilege to give many such lectures. There were however two eponymous lectures that gave me special pleasure, The Ivor Lewis and the Ernest Miles Memorial Lectures.

The name of Ivor Lewis has already been mentioned. During his work in a non-teaching hospital in London he made great advances in the treatment of oesophageal cancer and has had the distinction of devising an operation which bears his name and which helps to perpetuate his memory. In his later years he elected to work, and finally to retire, in his native Wales. It was in Wales that I was invited by a brilliant young surgeon, Christopher Davies,* to give the Ivor Lewis Memorial Lecture in 1985.

It was a great pleasure to pay tribute to the work of Ivor Lewis and the lecture was enhanced greatly by the presence of Sir Geoffrey Slaney, the President of the Royal College of Surgeons of England (Fig. 32). I was particularly privileged to have details of the life of Ivor Lewis which had been obtained by Dr Buddug Owen† who is a consultant anaesthetist and who knew Ivor Lewis well. She anaesthetized for Ivor Lewis and after his death in 1982 raised the money for the annual memorial lecture. The first Ivor Lewis Lecture being given by Professor Philip Stell‡ of Liverpool.

As a young doctor I had heard of the skills of a London surgeon, Ernest Miles. His name was legend and his operative skills had gained a reputation that was international. The Miles operation for cancer of the rectum was accepted as the standard of surgical currency. Strangely enough he wrote little of his work but, as a doer rather than a teacher, his fame was well established. In my wildest dream as a young surgeon I had never thought that I would be asked to give a lecture in his memory.

The Memorial Lecture was delivered in Liverpool to the British Association of Surgical Oncology and was entitled, "Adventures on a Surgical Everest".[24] It described the development of the McKeown

---

* Christopher Davies, D.M., M.Ch, F.R.C.S., Consultant Surgeon, Rhyl District General Hospital.

† Dr Buddug Owen, O.B.E., Consultant Anaesthetist.

‡ Professor Philip Stell, M.Ch., F.R.C.S., Professor of Oto-Rhino-Laryngology. University of Liverpool.

operation for gullet cancer and the other special discoveries made during the development of this operation.

It is interesting to note that in the pursuit of any scientific project, observations and discoveries are made which are not directly related to the project but may turn out to be of equal importance. These discoveries are referred to as "spin offs" and were a significant feature of the American space programme and the landing of astronauts on the moon.

In a very much smaller way discoveries were made when developing techniques for removal of cancer of the gullet which could be referred to as "surgical spin offs".

When operating on cancer at the lower end of the gullet it was realized that the adrenal glands could be more easily reached from the front rather than from the back which was at this time the accepted surgical approach. This led to the description of the anterior approach for removal of these glands for reasons completely unconnected with cancer of the oeso-phagus.[35]

Similarly, when developing the three-phase operation for cancer of the middle of the gullet, observations were made on the amount of saliva which a patient secretes each day, but more importantly it was observed that fluid could be absorbed in significant amounts from the mouth and from the gullet.

It was, of course, known that certain hormones and drugs could be effective if held in the mouth and absorbed locally rather than being swallowed, while the instant fatal results of the absorption of cyanide in the mouth were well known. Yet there had been no quantitative studies of fluid absorbed from the mouth and from the gullet until this particular study was carried out. The results of this study have been used in a completely different field in the management of patients with obstruction of the bowel.[23]

I felt that a record of a lifetime of experience in the development of the surgical treatment of cancer at the upper part of the intestinal tract, would be appropriate to the memory of a great surgeon who had made such contributions to the treatment of cancer at the lower end of the intestinal tract. It was with great pleasure that I received a memento of this lecture which was a miniature bust of this great surgeon, and this is now one of my treasured possessions.

SURGEON AT LARGE

I have always believed that to attain surgical excellence it is necessary to concentrate activities in one or possibly two centres. In this respect I hope that the operative work at the Memorial Hospital in Darlington and at the Friarage Hospital in Northallerton were of equal merit. Inevitably, invitations to operate in other hospitals were received but pressure of work in former years precluded such visits.

After retirement, however, such visits became possible and invitations to operate at various teaching and District General Hospitals were accepted. Though most interesting and enjoyable it is not easy to operate in a strange theatre, and operating, like football, is easier on the home pitch. There were, however, two occasions which stand out in my memory. One was a visit to Leeds and the other to Liverpool.

The case in Leeds was very unusual in that in removing a growth from the lower end of the gullet both, the left and right chest had to be opened up. This was formerly a procedure thought to be fraught with great danger but in actual fact the patient tolerated this unusual operation very well.

In Liverpool I had the great pleasure of assisting Professor Philip Stell to carry out the removal of the pharynx (lower part of the throat), after I had prepared the stomach to replace the gullet and the part of the throat which had been removed for a cancer. His technique of pharyngectomy was meticulous and superb and it was for me a very great pleasure to watch this master surgeon.

Lecturing, operating and writing have fully filled each day of retirement, and the more leisured atmosphere has added greatly to the enjoyment of this active and unusual period of life. Away from the stress and strain of obligatory duties, there is a freedom of thought and a freedom of speech, which is not available to those who are working entirely in the confines of the National Health Service. Perhaps this period has produced a unique opportunity to think unfettered by medical politics and to be able to speak the truth without fear.

26

The New Citadel

I N the days of Cronin's *The Citadel* there was a stability and dignity
in the profession of medicine. Advances in medicine and surgery were
taking place but the pace was steady and there was time to absorb the
new advances and to adjust to change. With all human activity there are
shortcomings and so it was with the medical profession but there was
merit in its stability and in its conservatism. Its flexibility was sufficient
to cope with two world wars with efficiency and on occasion with
heroism.

The massive army casualties of the Western Front were dealt with by
the Royal Army Medical Corps in the 1914–1918 war while the high
civilian casualties in the Second Wold War were coped with by the
Emergency Medical Service with an absolute minimum of administrative
staff and no managers. Tribute and respect is due to the doctors and
nurses of this former era.

The foundations of the new citadel were laid in 1948, with the introduction of the National Health Service by Aneurin Bevan and the socialist
government. At this time political influence began in a major way to
intervene in health considerations. On these original foundations of a
"free" medical service to all at the time of need, many changes have taken
place in the structure and philosophy of the Health Service. These
changes have been brought about by three factors; the unprecedented
advances and success in medicine, the financial implications of sophisticated treatment in patients whose expectations in treatment and cure are
high, and in changing political influences.

Discovery and invention have been the two cardinal features of
scientific advance. Unforeseen consequences in transport, industry and

engineering resulted from a single invention, that of the wheel which was made centuries ago.

In modern times discovery and invention have occurred not in a single, but in many fields. These advances which have taken place in biochemistry, physics, electronics and cellular biology have had a profound effect on medical science and in the practice of medicine. The multi-focal points of discovery and invention have produced greater advances in the past few decades than have taken place in all the centuries since the birth of Hippocrates, the father of modern medicine.

The discovery of D.N.A. and advances in the study of genetics have led to developments of medical techniques which have produced both legal and ethical problems undreamed of in former years. Genetic engineering can lead to difficult ethical and moral problems, while artificial insemination and surrogacy raise legal and ethical problems that have not yet been completely solved.

It is now medically possible to enable a woman long past the normal child bearing period, to have a baby at a time when old age is approaching. This produces a dilemma in which to forbid a patient the right to have a child is as wrong as to allow a woman to bear a child at a time when natural processes would make this impossible.

Most problems in life occur because of failure in its various forms, but in medicine it is the astonishing successes of the past fifty years that have given rise to difficulties that now confront the nations of the western world.

A triad of problems confronts the modern doctor. Life saving procedures are possible but are expensive in money and in time. The very success of these treatments results in the economic consequences of an ageing population. A third factor that has emerged in recent decades is that of patient expectation. In the multitudes of medical marvels each individual patient expects to have a personal benefit from recent advances, and becomes more demanding in a scenario of limited financial resources.

It is a strange irony that the stress produced by the increasing demands of patients should fall on the doctor and not on the politician, for it is indeed the politician in the National Health Service who controls the financial resources and therefore rations the expectations of treatment.

In these circumstances it is strangely inconsistent to draw up a charter of rights for patients, when it is known that financial stringency may well prevent the attainment of the objectives of the Patients Charter and the blame for failure falls on the doctor and not on the politician.

In former years the close relationship of trust between the patient and the doctor was an essential of medical practice. With the introduction of the National Health Service a third element of political control arose and has produced a triangular relationship.

In the undoubted initial success of the National Health Service, which became the envy of many countries, British politicians could happily bathe in the sunshine of success with little acknowledgement to the doctors and nurses who worked with such diligence to provide such a high standard of patient care. The unprecedented advances of medicine have, however, caused much political embarrassment as demand for treatment exceeds supply while the costs of complex treatment have steadily increased over the years.

It is perhaps appropriate that the problems outlined in the introductory chapter should now be re-considered so as to assess how the challenges of the National Health Service have been dealt with in the past forty-five years.

REORGANIZATIONS

To meet these problems different governments have attempted to solve the difficulties of the Health Service. Though science has made great advances, and each advance is built on previous experience, human behaviour however reverts to the base line in each generation.

It is not surprising that the problems facing the National Health Service have been met in a similar manner to that referred to by the Roman Governor of Britain 2,000 years ago. Attempts at solving these problems have been by reorganizations, each of which has caused changes in the development of a New Citadel. All these reforms have up to the present time been technical and none has interfered with the fundamental concept of a health service free at the time of delivery, and in which financial considerations played virtually no part.

There is little doubt that in former years many of the changes and reorganizations were cosmetic and were introduced to create a feeling of progress, while not addressing the problems consequent on medical progress and success in the treatment of disease. In this illusion a new language or jargon has evolved. A member of the service who is employed as a planner has now assumed a much more prestigious title such as Director of Corporate Strategy, and a personnel officer has now become a Director of Human Resources.

With such distinguished titles an infrastructure of staff seems inevitable so that there is a proliferation of administration which is irrespective of the amount of work done. As Professor Parkinson has pointed out administrators create work for themselves and are anxious that this additional work is carried out by subordinates, so that a pyramidal structure of administration is created. This has been a characteristic feature of the hospital service over the past forty years.

When I was appointed Senior Consultant Surgeon at Darlington Memorial Hospital there was only one administrator, now there are dozens.

It is true to say that the work has somewhat increased over this period and a completely new hospital has been built but the increase in administrative staff far exceeds the increase in the service provided. Even committees proliferate, blossom and fade only to scatter seeds from which new committees and quangos will germinate. There is no doubt that administration begets administrators, so that the Health Service is scourged with more Chiefs and fewer and fewer Indians.

It is estimated by the Audit Commission, under the Chairmanship of Sir David Cooksey, that in the last five years the wage bill for hospital managers has risen by 1,700 per cent. In actual figures and allowing for inflation the bill has risen from £11 million to £251 million over the period of five years to April, 1991. Over the corresponding period the nursing staff has only increased from 428,000 to 431,000 an increase of under one per cent.

It is therefore true that more money is being spent on the Health Service, but it is on administration rather than on those who care for the sick.

THE HEALTH MARKET

The changes in the National Health Service introduced by the Government in April 1991 were however of an entirely new and revolutionary kind and a far cry from the former concepts on which the National Health Service was founded in 1948. For the very first time market forces have been introduced into the National Health Service. It is true to say that the early signs of this change were the contracting out of hospital laundry and cleaning services, and this was the thin edge of the wedge.

The extension of market forces into clinical medicine is revolutionary in England and has produced an impact the reverberations of which are yet to be fully realized, and the government, like the sorcerer's apprentice, may have liberated forces over which it has no control.

In former years the global sum allocated to the Health Service was divided amongst each of the fourteen hospital regions. In response to submissions from the District Hospital Management Committees each district in the region had its allocation from which it was to provide the services to the district.

The completely new concept is that the Health Service is a market place, where there are purchasers and providers of health care. Health care is therefore a commodity that can be bought and sold, and the National Health Service has been transformed into the *National Health Market*. This concept of health as a commodity is obvious to most doctors, and is now becoming obvious to the ordinary man in the street.

A new terminology has been introduced to reinforce the atmosphere of commerce in medicine. For generations past, people consulting doctors were referred to as patients, just as those seeking legal advice were referred to as clients, while in ecclesiastical circles attenders at church were regarded as parishioners. The word patient is a very special term that indicates the unique relationship which exists between an ill person and his doctor, and its use is time honoured.

With the commercial changes in the Health Service, and with encouragement from the Department of Health, the staff in hospitals and in general practice are encouraged to refer to patients as customers. It is sad to see the usage of such a rich language as English degraded in this way and the time honoured word patient replaced by a word associated

253

with commerce. I believe that this term is rather like the mule which has neither pride of ancestry nor hope of posterity.

The whole new phraseology which is being forced on those who work in the Health Service is now referred to as Health Speak. It is, I believe, the product of an administration, sterile of ideas, and seeking an identity.

MARKET FORCES

It is interesting to note that the Government appears to be dedicated to market forces. In another sphere, the contemporary report on the police service (The Sheehy Report) recommends similar changes in the police to those being introduced into the Health Service.

Performance related pay is recommended. But in the absence of parameters to measure performance this will prove as difficult, or as impossible, in the police service as it will in medicine. Short term contracts, introduced to weed out the very small proportion of lazy or inefficient staff, will deter recruitment by producing insecurity in those who wish to make a career in any particular service. The fact is that the concept of a *service* is being decimated by a doctrine of *market forces*, so that the National Health Service has become the National Health Market.

There are few stockbrokers who can accurately forecast industrial market trends. In adopting a market strategy Government have embarked on a course with no greater certainty of success in medical care than an investor dealing in the stock market. Inevitably there have been successes and failures, fulfilment and disappointment. The establishment of market forces has produced many unexpected results, and like Pandora's Box many demons have been liberated which government can not now control. The reform has been described by the B.M.A. as an uncontrolled monster cheating patients and demoralizing doctors.

Essential to the business strategy in health care is the establishment of budgets, and these can affect both general practice and the hospital service. The result of this is to transfer the responsibility for using the budget from central to peripheral control. If there is a short-fall of financial resources and rationing of medical services becomes necessary, then the responsibility for this will fall on the general practitioner who is a budget holder, or on the hospital which has Trust status.

Initially in general practice the budget allocations have been generous indeed and have been an inducement for doctors to become budget holders. They are therefore able, at the present time, to manage their affairs in the way they feel is most appropriate. On the other hand, should the present industrial depression continue then the Treasury allocation of funds may be cut back and further rationing of medical services would become necessary, not only in general practice, but also in the hospital service.

GENERAL PRACTICE

Family doctors are now divided into two groups, those who are fund-holders and those who are not. The larger practices with many partners tend to be in fund-holding practices, while the single handed and small group practices are non–fund–holders.

Perhaps the most unexpected result of the introduction of market forces has been to increase the power of those general practitioners who are fund-holders and have to keep within their budgets. As a budget-holder the practitioner has the attractive option to shop around and select the hospital from which he wishes to buy his services for his patient and which provides, as he sees it, the best value for money. As he is paying for the treatment he can attempt to demand in the contract with the hospital that his patients should be seen at a specific time and within a stated period. If the local district hospital can not meet the demands of the general practitioner then a contract can be made with another hospital which may well be at a much greater distance from the patient's home.

On the other hand, a G.P. who is not a budget-holder is at a disadvantage since he does not have the financial muscle to have his request met by the hospital or the Health Authority.

In the Darlington and Northallerton areas, for example, patients of budget-holding practices can have a cataract operation within two months at a local private hospital, whereas non-budget-holders' patients have to wait for up to two years for treatment in a N.H.S. hospital. In addition, hospital managers are putting pressure on consultants to treat patients from fund-holding practices because of the financial considerations. In spite of much political denial preferential treatment for fund-holding practices is widespread. This is presently referred to as fast tracking since patients from fund-holding practices are, as it were, put into the fast lane for hospital treatment.

It is apparent now that a two tier system has evolved in general practice and which many doctors had foreseen and about which the British Medical Association has sounded a warning. It is interesting to contemplate however, what will happen when non-budget-holders combine together to become budget-holders and become equally demanding so that a one tier system is again restored with no increase in resources.

With the new found power of the general practitioners to shop around and send their patients, for whatever reason, to a more distant hospital, the advantage and even the existence of the local District Hospital could be endangered. Most referrals to distant hospitals will be made largely on grounds of the possibility of an early out-patient consultation or of a short waiting list, and not necessarily on the quality or skill of surgical care.

It used to be said that a patient wishing to have the highest standard of surgical treatment should go to the surgeon with the longest waiting list. This may be still as true today as it was years ago.

It would be wrong to risk the closure of a District General Hospital providing excellent care on grounds that it was unable to compete in the reduction of waiting lists for operations or out-patient consultation times. The outcome of treatment is far more important than the waiting time for treatment. It was my experience while in London, that after super-human efforts for several months to reduce a tonsil waiting list, after an initial reduction, it was frustrating to find that the list just grew once again to the same level as previously.

It is a situation which is already arising again in the "waiting list initiative" of the present day of which there is much political publicity. The waiting list has become a sort of "gold standard" in hospital performance. This is a most erroneous concept, and may lead to the loss of some excellent hospitals throughout the country.

There are however other consequences affecting clinical management of patients which are disturbing. When a consultant has seen a case and made a recommendation regarding treatment such as an operation, then the general practitioner has to pay for the operation and may not wish to give approval for financial or other reasons. This is a situation in which a consultant, if his advice is not followed, would be justified in not accepting further responsibility for the patient and his or her management. Similarly a consultant may wish to call in a fellow consultant for further advice. The general practitioner may not agree and may not wish to encroach further on his budget, so that for financial reasons advice and treatment may be curtailed.

Many general practitioners now make the request for the consultant to see cases in the general practitioner's surgery. This is of great convenience to the general practitioner though not necessarily to his patient. The close association between the general practitioner and the consultant engendered by this arrangement is very desirable but is very wasteful of that very valuable commodity, consultant's time.

It is far better, and of wider value to all general practitioners, if the consultant sees the patients in his Out-Patient Clinic at hospital where he has all the appropriate facilities for diagnosis and for record keeping. In teaching and in clinical research out-patients also form an essential part of the medical structure. Follow up reviews are most important in observing and assessing the results of treatment and in audit.

To fragment this system by encouraging the out-patient aspect of consultant work to be carried out in various general practitioners' surgeries would be highly detrimental to the practice of medicine.

In addition, budgetary considerations may impede re-attendance at hospital and the carrying out of investigative procedures which are an essential part of clinical research, and if research is impeded clinical management will be impaired and the patient will suffer. This encroachment into the out-patient hospital clinic on grounds of finance or general practitioner convenience is a serious threat to patient care, medical teaching and clinical research.

Before the National Health Service was instituted general practitioner surgeons practised widely throughout the entire country. Since the introduction of the National Health Service provided a universally available consultant surgical service available to all patients, the need for the general practitioner surgeon has been removed. It was in fact one of the major benefits of the National Health Service that it provided a consultant surgical service throughout the entire country.

Of recent date the Minister of Health has reverted to this former state and has encouraged general practitioners to again engage in minor surgery. The intended political effect is to cut down hospital waiting lists. But with budget-holding practices, where the general practitioner is paid to do operations, there may be a tendency to extend the range of procedures carried out by the general practitioner beyond his scope, rather than pay for them to be done by a consultant in an National Health Service hospital or in a private hospital.

It would be difficult to decide if any general practitioner is operating in a field outside his complete competence, and the re-introduction of the general practitioner surgeon may set the clock back forty years.

HOSPITAL SERVICE

In the hospital service, as in general practice, there are those hospitals which are fund holding and those which are funded. The term Trust Hospital is used for those hospitals which have their own budget and which have financial independence. But problems may well arise in such Trust Hospitals which will affect the practice of other hospitals who do not have Trust status.

In Trust Hospitals which have financial independence there may well be a tendency to concentrate on procedures that are not too costly and to leave the more difficult conditions to be treated in a District General Hospital which does not have Trust status. This could mean that the elderly and those suffering from the more complex diseases and requiring prolonged treatment could be at a disadvantage. This was a scenario which was present in London before the war where the Teaching Hospital dealt with the more glamorous aspects of medicine and the old and the chronically ill patients gravitated to the London County Council (L.C.C.) hospitals in what was a two tier hospital system.

Of more recent date there has been a most hopeful sign emerging in some Trust Hospitals. They are encouraging limited private practice in their hospitals and facilitating patients who have health insurance plans. This increases the trust income and allows money to become available to N.H.S. patients.

This is exactly the same concept that I outlined to some Conservative politicians at the Carlton Club on 28 April 1969. If only this policy had been followed the purchaser provider arrangement, with all its managers, administrators and accountants, would had been avoided and immense sums of money saved. I believe, too, that the morale of the profession would have been boosted.

WAITING LISTS

Waiting lists for surgical operations have been a problem that has been present long before the inception of the National Health Service. With the involvement of the N.H.S. as a political issue the size of the waiting list has been used as an index of failure of the service to provide what patients have required and what patients are now demanding. It is, however, erroneous to consider a hospital with a long waiting list as a poor hospital and the converse is often true.

The size of a waiting list does not rest entirely on the shoulders of the medical and nursing professions as most recent events have shown. In the hospitals with which I am associated my colleagues in orthopaedic surgery are being pressed by the managers to increase the number of hip replacements and are willing and able to do so, but are restricted from doing so by the same administration who have to keep within their budgets and have run out of money. The frustration of being, on the one hand, pressed to increase an already heavy load and, on the other hand, being prevented from doing so is causing much discontent in surgical circles.

Many hospitals throughout the country have already fulfilled block contracts by December or have run out of money so that wards and operating theatres are closed and all but emergency or paying patients are cancelled until the commencement of the new financial year.

The advice of the Minister is to spin out the cases over a longer period, which is another way of saying, "please conceal the fact that the consultants are not allowed to fulfil their full potential because of shortage of funds". It is in fact a technique of concealment of the rationing of medical care by strict adherence to a budget, while at the same time the public is led to believe that there will be no *rationing* of medical care within the National Health Service.

The medical profession well recognizes that resources are finite and limited, but they are also doctors aware of the clinical needs of patients. In former years clinical need was considered to be of paramount importance but things have changed and now financial considerations are being forced on the profession.

In addition to this, attempting to adhere to the Patients Charter introduces a further dimension of time on the waiting list, which may result in non-urgent cases being awarded a higher priority for admission than the clinical condition deserves. A patient with varicose veins, for example, who had been waiting for two years will gain priority over a patient who suffers indigestion and abdominal symptoms due to gall bladder disease. It is a great mistake to promise under the National Health Service fulfilments of a charter in the absence of adequate resources.

MANAGEMENT

The Profession realizes that skilful management of limited resources is essential to make the best use of what funds are available. The misconception that doctors are poor managers has been fostered in some quarters, when the fact is that with the fascinating challenges of medicine they prefer to be doctors rather than to be managers. What the doctor wants is for someone to facilitate his or her clinical skills so that he can concentrate on patient care and not be diverted to administrative problems which can be undertaken by someone of more limited skills and training.

To meet this situation Government has made a well intentioned and serious attempt to institute a series of directorates within the hospital structure. These consist of a clinical director and a manager. This should be conducive to providing care of the patient combined with efficient use of resources. This system can work so long as the manager acts as a catalyst to the clinician and that most of the available resources are directly for patient care. Management for management's sake is sterile, expensive and unproductive. A proliferation of managers is a "cancer" striking at the very heart of the hospital service. If in some hypothetical catastrophe all managers and administrators were to be lost, the medical and nursing professions would, I am sure, continue with the work of healing the sick. There is, however, no doubt that good clinicians can be helped by good management but good management of itself is of no benefit to patients. Management is not polyvalent and it is important to realize that a very special type of manager is required to work in the special environment of a hospital.

Mistakes in the past have arisen from extrapolating administrative procedures from pure industry into the hospital service, and it is important not to repeat the errors once again in this field.

THE EFFECT OF CHANGE

Gradual change from season to season is smooth and causes no undue problems but sudden changes cause storms and are disruptive, and so it is in other situations where evolution is replaced by revolution. Over the forty years since the introduction of the National Health Service there have been evolutionary changes. The recent reforms of 1991 are however, revolutionary, and like climatic storms have caused chaos.

In spite of this the service has continued rather as a punch-drunk boxer goes on fighting—as this is what he is trained to do. The present position in the Health Service and in the profession is unsettled and unstable and some of the results of the recent reorganization are becoming apparent.

The first effect is a change in philosophy where cost and financial considerations appear to take precedence over the clinical need of the patient. When I first began to deal with cases of cancer of the gullet, the question was, "Can this patient be cured and do I have the skills to do so?" The question of cost was never considered, though it was quite apparent that to cure ten young working men suffering from rupture was economically more profitable than curing a seventy-five year old man with a cancer of the gullet. Yet the challenge of dealing with a cancer was much more attractive than the lesser task of repairing a hernia.

The second major change has been in development of division within the medical and the nursing professions. The provider and purchaser open market procedures have produced divisions amongst the doctors and others concerned with patient care. The relationship between the general practitioners and the consultants is less close than formerly, and increasing general practitioner power has put the consultants under greater pressure than ever before. This, together with demands to meet the requirements of the Patients Charter, and the demands and expectations of the patients themselves, is causing great strain and discontent in the consultant ranks.

There is also a division in general practice itself, where the fund-holding practices are getting a better share of the medical resources than those that are not fund-holders.

This condition is likely to continue until the present generous budgets become scaled down as the result of financial stringency or when all practices become fund-holders. Similarly, in the hospital service, there is also division between the hospital Trusts and those hospitals that do not have Trust status. This may resolve if all hospitals gain equality of status.

In the hospital service itself there are at present many different problems. It is accepted that a consultant takes the ultimate responsibility for a patient but they do not now have the power to implement their wishes. The position of power has moved largely to management and administration, but the consultant is still forced to accept the responsibility.

The position of responsibility without power is in principle unacceptable.

Paperwork has increased enormously and attempting to meet various government imposed initiatives adds greatly to the work of a profession which has long been over burdened. Clinical philosophy has been replaced by accountant philosophy and it is felt generally that this has reduced the standard of patient care.

The clinician sees all around him increase in the administrative staff while in medicine and in nursing there is chronic staff shortage. Recent attempts by lay staff to monitor the performance of consultants has caused much trouble and unhappiness in the profession.

While clinical audit and peer review are certainly welcomed, managerial assessment of performance is considered completely inappropriate. It has always been felt that there has been a strong trust in the integrity of the profession and there is no reason to believe that this trust has in any way been misplaced.

In general terms there is developing a deep sense of division between those involved in clinical care and those in management and a "them" and "us" situation has developed for the first time and this is unsatisfactory and divisive. The present emphasis on budget, on business and on bureaucracy are the three Bs which threaten the Health Service in Britain today. I am reminded of the two domes of the cathedral in Benghazi which I first saw when I was in army service in the Middle East. I was told that the two domes were symbolic of an ecclesiastical division whereas the single dome of St. Paul's in London and St. Peter's in Rome represented a united church.

It is to be hoped that the long tradition of a united profession in medicine and in nursing will soon return.

Perhaps the most serious effect of hurried change has been to increase the strain on doctors who already have to bear great burdens by the very nature of the work. It is not perhaps surprising that there is much unhappiness in those who care for the sick. This seems to pervade all those involved in clinical medicine and affects both doctors and nurses.

In this last year many distinguished surgeons who have made great contributions to the treatment of disease, have told me of their great longing to retire and get out of medicine as it is in Britain today. This is indeed a remarkable feature, since surgeons in particular require a dedication to their work, to enable them to continue in this most demanding of all occupations. There is something radically wrong with a system which has caused this change of heart.

In the half century in which I have been in practice I have never experienced a period in which morale in the profession was so low and paradoxically the euphoria among some politicians so high.

Having observed the great brain drain of former years, anxiety for the future of medicine in Britain is understandable. While addressing a world conference held by the U.I.C.C. (International Union Against Cancer) in Buenos Aries some years ago, of the five opening speakers four were graduates of the United Kingdom who are now working in other parts of the world. This is an example of the brain drain from Britain.

Medicine is truly international, and if in any community a profession is impeded or imposed on, migration is the result. It is therefore necessary to preserve and encourage our brain power within the United Kingdom and to encourage and to facilitate the work of the clinician. In the final analysis, clinicians should be paramount and administration or management must play a facilitating role to enable them to do their job in the best possible circumstances.

Managerial dictation should have no part in medicine, and it is the clinical need which is paramount. There is a great deal of individualism in medicine and even in what might be called "teams" the team is usually found to contain an outstanding leader at its nucleus.

THE FORGOTTEN FACTOR

The vast majority of doctors regard medicine as a calling as well as an occupation. In a similar way people are attracted into the services, into the Church or even to become a missionary in foreign lands.

In my own case it was the incident with the girl injured in the sleighing accident that made me make the decision to be a doctor. Though I realized that doctors were reasonably well off the question of financial reward never crossed my mind, even though in my early boyhood I had observed at first hand the hardships of the industrial depression after the First World War.

Having graduated as a doctor it was only then that I realized that to become a specialist surgeon required an immense academic effort together with years of training and long hours of duty that the vast majority of people would not for one moment contemplate.

The attainment of consultant status, while providing a reasonable income, is not comparable with that in other walks of life where the rewards are far higher and the responsibilities far less. There is, however, a compensation in the respect which the position commands and the trust that it inspires.

It is perhaps in the question of trust that the recent changes in the Health Service have provoked the most offence. The constant intrusion of managers indicates an incipient underlying distrust in the integrity of the consultant, whereas in former years the N.H.S. has always relied on complete trust in the medical profession.*

The N.H.S. has survived because consultants work far and away beyond their contracts and though obtaining information about work and patients is important, any kind of surveillance which undermines the

---

* The N.H.S. Reform So Far. Klein R. Ann. Royal Coll. Surgeons of England (1993) 75:74–78

sense of dedication would be a disaster. Health care demands dedication and should inspire trust.

Intrinsic to the profession of medicine is the element of job satisfaction. Recent reviews* suggest that job satisfaction has fallen from eighty-eight per cent to forty-seven per cent on the introduction of the recent reforms. Of doctors who qualified before 1984, one in seven now regret their choice of career, while those who qualified after 1987, one third regret that they have become doctors. The new changes in the Health Service may result in a change in the type of doctor who might now be more materialistic, while the more dedicated doctor may disappear.

The ethos and dedication of the profession has not been taken into consideration in the business changes that have been introduced and this feature has been the forgotten factor.

The present Citadel is founded on market forces and resource management. There is a feeling in the government that market forces will act as a constant regulator of the Health Service and make additions and adjustments as the needs arise. In other fields, such as industry, market forces have resulted in boom and depression and we are at present experiencing a severe international depression.

It would seem, therefore, that market forces may not be the panacea that present political thinking seems to indicate. On the other hand, the rigid system of controlled economy of the communist states has been unsuccessful. It would seem that some amalgam of the two systems, that I suggested to the Carlton Club some twenty years ago, may provide the most appropriate system for the control and availability of medical services.

The worship of Resource Management (R.M.) has produced a fantastic increase in management and a diminution of clinical resources at a time when there is an ever increasing demand for ever increasing medical treatment. Hopefully, with the passage of time, any real advantages of the new changes will be retained, while the less successful will be discarded. It may well be that the purchaser-and-provider concept will be discarded as, up to the present time, it has caused so much confusion and distress.

* Hospital Doctor. Day M. Sick and Tired (1993) 13:1–16

The political worship of a market philosophy, while understandable, has displaced the philosophy of service and is alien to a profession which depends on dedication and integrity.

The Citadel of today is gigantic and employs the greatest work force in Europe. Organization and management require great skill and insight. The recent changes in the Health Service have achieved only some of their objectives, but have unfortunately resulted in an impairment in the spirit of service in a dedicated work force and its replacement by the philosophy of commerce.

The ever advancing frontiers of medicine have overstrained the resources of an economy that can no longer afford to keep pace and to provide all the medical services that have become possible. With present limitations of resources for medical care cut backs are inevitable.

Unfortunately, these cut backs have fallen on those of the clinical work force, so that many highly trained technicians are losing their jobs, while administration and management proliferate. Even those who have spent years of hard work in training to attain consultant status are to lose security at the end of the line by being offered short term contracts.

In the days of Cronin's *The Citadel* the profession itself determined its own standards and ethos. Step by step, the Citadel arose and was maintained by a professional code of conduct. In spite of some frailities there is no doubt that the profession was patient orientated and that the clinical needs were paramount. It is understandable that, with the advent of the National Health Service in 1948, there was considerable apprehension about the profession's future and there was a conservative resistence to change. But political influences were to prevail with the co-operation of the profession the National Health Service was a great success and was the envy of many countries.

In the new Citadel the situation is somewhat different. In broad principle, providing medical treatment has now become a business and the words and ethos of industry are being encouraged to pervade the whole service and even its nomenclature. There is no doubt that in the first Citadel the profession was somewhat resistent to change and was defensive in its position. Today the position is very different and it is the politicians who are on the defensive. The revolutionary changes in principle and management recently introduced, without first having a pilot study, have created problems that had not been contemplated.

266

It is, therefore, not surprising there is great sensitivity in political circles regarding the effects of the recent changes in the Health Service. Constant emphasis on the increasing expenditure on the Health Service, on the number of patients treated, and "better treatment" are reiterated by those involved in the hope of presenting a favourable public image. The perception of those who actually work in the Health Service is completely different. Increasing expenditure is obvious to all but this expenditure is on managers and administrative staff. These have, as already mentioned, increased by 1,700 per cent in the last five years whilst increase in the nursing staff is less than one per cent. The figures for the number of patients treated is also suspect. The system of counting "clinical episodes" rather than the number of patients treated leads to distortion of the figures and gives the impression that the numbers treated are actually greater than before and this is misleading. There is no doubt that many patients are better treated than formerly but this is purely due to medical advances and not to the new systems of management. In real patient care most will agree that the physical and emotional care of the patient now is less than formerly. The situation is regarded with despair by those who actually work in it.

The Citadel described by Cronin could be regarded as a fortress to protect the medical profession, the Citadel of today is designed to dominate it.

Epilogue

L IFE is a one lap race and there is no opportunity to live it again other than in memory. Privileged by a long life, and blessed with a good memory I have been able to relive the life and times of a surgeon.

The period is unique in medical advances, and in social and political change. It covers two world wars, and two industrial depressions. The depression of the early years after the First World War, and the contemporary depression which is affecting all countries in the West.

Of special interest are the changes that have occurred in medicine. The discovery of antibiotics has reduced the great death rate from tuberculosis and from bacterial disease, while programmes of immunization have reduced poliomyelitis (infantile paralysis) and eradicated small-pox throughout the world. But all viral disease is not yet conquered and AIDS presents a potential hazard to the health of the world. Degenerative disease of joints is dealt with by replacement and kidney degenerative disease can be dealt with by kidney transplant. In degenerative diseases of the heart and the arteries surgical procedures have been most successful and now even heart transplants are becoming almost routine.

It is, however, in malignant disease that the long-looked for breakthrough is still eagerly awaited. Though surgery, radiotherapy and chemotherapy have individually or in combination made great advances, cancer still is one of the great killers.

The greater involvement of political influences in medicine has made an impact in medicine and in the medical profession. The days of Cronin's *The Citadel* regarded by some as an edifice for the protection for the professional interest are gone and a new Citadel has arisen. It is a new Citadel in which politics, state involvement and the inevitable bureaucracy play a prominent part. Market forces have displaced the medical ethics of former years.

In the days of Cronin's *The Citadel* there was complete freedom to criticize the system or establishment, and his famous book is testament to this freedom. But with increasing political and state control on medicine any criticism of the New Citadel by those who now work within it could have serious consequences for the critic. Regulations are afoot to muzzle free speech in the Health Service, and those who speak out about shortcomings may well have the proposed short-term contracts terminated. This is perhaps one of the most disturbing features to those dedicated professions who are responsible for the caring of the sick.

In this autobiography one can recall the events from the early youthful enthusiasm of entering a career in medicine right up to the present day.

It has been a great privilege to work as a surgeon in what, in retrospect, were the halcyon days. It is true that a lifetime in practice as a consultant surgeon has given great insight into people and politics, but it is the recollection of the success in the treatment of disease that has given the author the pleasure of roses in December.

References

1. Joint Working Party on Organization of Medical Work in Hospitals, Report. H.M.S.O. 1967, 1972, 1974.

2. Griffiths, The Griffiths Report.

3. Guillou P. J., The potential impact of immuno-biochemistry on Cancer Therapy. *Brit. J. Surg.* 1987; 74:705–710.

4. McKeown K. C., Multiple Primary Malignant Neoplasms. *Euro. J. Surg. Oncology* 1991; 17:429–446.

5. Fraser I., *Blood Sweat and Cheers*. BMA Publication. University Press. Cambridge.

6. Ministry of Health, Report into an outbreak of Typhoid Fever, 1939. H.M.S.O.

7. McKeown K. C., The conservative treatment of Osteo-myelitis. *Proc. R. Soc. Med.* 1942; 35:215–229.

8. McKeown K. C., The role of chemotherapy in Haematogenous Osteo-myelitis. *Brit. J. Surg.* 1943; 121:13–18.

9. McKeown K. C., The history of the Diabetic Foot. *The Foot* 1992; 2:179–182.

10. Boulton A. J., Lawrence Lecture. The Diabetic Foot, neuropathy and aetiology. *Diabetic Medicine* 1990; 7:852–858.

11. Stratton B., *Island of Terrible Friends* 1961 Hodder & Stoughton. London

12. Murley, *Surgical Roots and Branches* 1990. British Medical Association Publication.

13. Aird I., *Companion in Surgical Studies* 1957. Edinburgh. Livingstone.

14. Porritt A., and Hanfield-Jones R. H. *Essentials of Modern Surgery*. 5th Edition. 1938.

15. Harker C., *Call Me Matron*. Heinemann. London 1980.

16. Pickles, *Epidemiology in General Practice.*

17. McKeown K. C., A study of Peptic Ulcer with special reference to the results of Partial Gastrectomy. *Brit. J. Surg* 1962; 220:231.

18. McKeown K. C., A prospective study of the immediate and long term results of Polya Gastrectomy in Duodenal Ulcer. *Brit. J. Surg.* 1972; 59:849–868.

19. McKeown K. C., (1969) *Total Oesophagectomy for Carcinoma*, British Medical Association Film No: 438.

20. McKeown K. C., (1972) Trends in Oesophageal Resection for Carcinoma with special reference to Total Oesophagectomy. (Hunterian Lecture) *Ann. Royal College of Surgeons England* 1951; 213–230.

21. McKeown K. C., (1985) The surgical treatment of Carcinoma of the Oesophagus. *Journal of Royal College of Surgeons of Edinburgh.* 30:1–14

22. McKeown K. C., *Operative Cancer Surgery*, (1992) Ed. Burn I and Wellwood J. McK, Farrand Press, London.

23. McKeown K. C. & Dunstone G. A., (1959) Some observations in salivary secretion and fluid absoption by mouth. *British Medical Journal* 2:670–672.

24. McKeown K. C., (1990) Adventures on a Surgical Everest (Ernest Miles Memorial Lecture). *European J. Surg. Onco.* 13. 375–381.

25. McKeown K. C., (1991) Multiple primary Malignant Neoplasms. *European J. Surg. Onco.* 17:429–446.

26. Orringer M. B. and Orringer J. G., (1983) Oesophagectomy without Thoracotomy. *J. Thor. and Cardio-Vascular Surgery* 85:72–80.

27. Silber W. Carcinoma of the Oesophagus. S. A. Medical Research Council.

28. Thatcher N., Digestive Cancer, *Advances in Medical Oncology.* U.I.C.C. Pergamon Press. Oxford 1978.

29. B.M.A. Board of Science and Education, *The Medical Effects of Nuclear War.* John Wiley and sons, Chichester.

30. Bichop D. G. M. and McKeown K. C., Oesophagectomy with Gastric Replacement. *Brit. J. Surg.* 66:810–819.

31. Taylor, Selwyn (ed.), *Surgical Management.* 1984. Heinemann & Co. London.

32. Taylor, Selwyn (ed.), *Recent Advances in Surgery.* 1972. Churchill.

33. Nyhus, Lloyd M. and Baker, Robert, *Mastery of Surgery.* 1984. Little Brown & Co. Boston, Toronto.

34. Burn, Ian and Wellwood K. McK. (eds.). *Operative Cancer Surgery.* 1993. Farrand Press.

35. The Anterior Approach for Bilateral Adrenalectomy. B. M. J. 1956.

Index